A NATURALIST IN TRINIDAD

A NATURALIST IN TRINIDAD

C. Brooke Worth

DRAWINGS BY DON R. ECKELBERRY

J. B. Lippincott Company
Philadelphia and New York

First edition

Printed in the United States of America

Library of Congress Catalog Card Number 67–11313

Contents

Contents 6

Illustrations

Maps

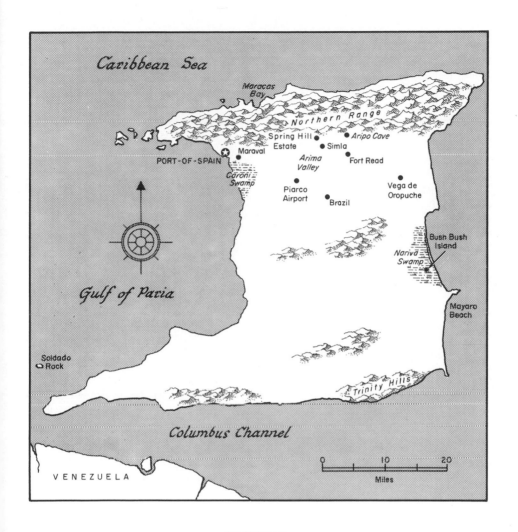

TRINIDAD

A NATURALIST IN TRINIDAD

Chapter 1

TRINIDAD!

I don't know how many of my ornithological friends back in the States would have given their right arms to be in my position to net birds in Trinidad for four and a half years, but I suspect all of them would have given at least some thought to it. No matter what their approach to bird study, the list makers would see this as a means of making certain identification of elusive species in the hand, while the more biologically oriented ones could immediately sense the value of information gained in a program of netting birds, banding and releasing them, and trapping them again on one or more subsequent occasions.

Bird students today are a different breed from those a generation ago, and for all time before that. The change may not be for the better, but it is there. Gilbert White could spend a lifetime in one garden. More recently Witmer Stone wrote two large volumes on *Bird Studies at Old Cape May*. The ornithology of exotic lands was not for them: travel was slow, health hazards were serious and unavoidable, and people simply had less money and leisure. Actually it did not occur to them that one should attempt to become more than a local expert in the woods near home.

I was one of the early rebels against that attitude. To me—an inveterate list maker but also with curiosity about biology—the avifauna of the entire world seemed enticing. My problem was to find some way to be paid for going on a global bird walk. When I graduated from Swarthmore College in 1931, the Depression was with us and sponsors were unimaginable. However, one could hope that a degree in medicine might lead to work in public health in far places, where birds would flit openly on week ends and even engage the corner of an eye during the week.

Things did not work out so easily. Perhaps I would have made faster progress if I had taken a Ph.D. in ornithology, but that seemed in 1931 to point to certain penury. My friend from Haverford College, Johnny Emlen, made it by that route, but he was still a bachelor. Merida and I were newly married, and we bought vegetables in a store where the clerk sported a Phi Beta Kappa key. It took about twenty-five years before I was able to set the alarm for 3 A.M. in Trinidad, grab a hasty breakfast, snatch up my binoculars and bird bands, and set up the Japanese mist nets at daybreak with the satisfaction of knowing that I was being paid for my joys.

Meanwhile my career had taken me to India and Africa. Not bad! But in those wonderful places I dealt with mosquitoes and small wild mammals (which I came to love dearly, too). In a way, the Ph.D. in ornithology might have been a hindrance, for it would have marked me as a specialist. As things turned out, I could not be classified on anybody's list as anything but a general biologist, and when opportunities arose to serve in any capacity whatsoever in a field project involving esoteric investigations in an unheard-of hinterland, my willingness to volunteer was not screened by degree sifters. In a sense I have been a fraud, for a true specialist could have improved on every job I have held. On the other hand, no single specialist would be likely to have been given such a variety of assignments. I am content.

Mist nets, binoculars, bird bands and—I forgot to say—needles! My joys are not purely aesthetic. This Golden-headed Manakin in my hand, just removed from the net, must now be bled from the jugular vein so that its serum can be tested by my colleagues at TRVL—the Trinidad Regional Virus Laboratory—in Port-of-Spain, West Indies.

TRVL was housed originally in a rickety old army barracks near the water front of Port-of-Spain. Among the numerous laboratory animals required for virus work, the mouse colony was most populous, at peak times holding many thousands of individuals. However cockroaches far outnumbered all other beasts put together, while invisible hordes of termites gnawed at the cheap timbers.

GOLDEN-HEADED MANAKIN

That was from 1953 to 1961—a long time during which to produce brilliant work in squalor. But that is the record. When I arrived in 1960, just before our move to the splendid new laboratory in Federation Park, my antecedent colleagues had already discovered a dozen or more new viruses.

The lab was founded, staffed and supported by the Rockefeller

Foundation and the governments of Great Britain and the several British West Indian islands, Trinidad being then still a colony. Therefore the senior scientific personnel shifted from time to time from one foreign post to another.

However, the Director until we occupied new quarters, Dr. Wilbur G. Downs, had been there from the outset. Wil was already an old acquaintance, for I had met him twenty years earlier when he arrived at the Army Medical School in Washington one day with a collection of Mallophaga—bird lice—from South Pacific battlefields. Between bombs, he had trained enlisted men on his antimalaria team in the arts of making bird skins and collecting vermin from the plumage.

Tommy, Dr. Thomas H. G. Aitken, arrived at the same time as Wil, but his official background was purely in entomology. They were equally versatile men and together set out to make a complete survey of Trinidad's animals and plants. Tommy is a great hiker and Boy Scout leader. There was soon not a major peak in Trinidad's Northern Range that he had not canvassed for orchids, bromeliads and tree ferns. His collection of bromeliads—"wild pineapples," "air plants"—repeatedly has won prizes at the annual exhibition of the Trinidad Horticultural Society.

Wil, Tommy and I were employees of the Rockefeller Foundation. So was Dr. Andries H. Jonkers, a new recruit who came to Trinidad in 1960 just when I did. Dries is Dutch, but he had spent several years in the States, obtaining a postgraduate doctoral degree in public health at Tulane University. He became the epidemiologist at TRVL, which means (in his own facetious words) that he "let us do the work and then sat to think about what we had done." Well, somebody had to make head or tail of all our data, and most of the time we were too busy gathering them to pause for sufficient reflection.

When Wil Downs left, Dr. Leslie P. Spence succeeded him. This was in line with Rockefeller practice, for Leslie belonged in the West Indies, having been born on the tiny island of St. Vincent in the Lesser Antilles. The Foundation moves in (on invitation) with its own personnel but within a limited number of years moves out, leaving behind a local staff to carry on. Leslie was admirably qualified for the post, having received his medical training in England and thereafter becoming proficient in virology and serology through a series of grants-in-aid for study in laboratories abroad. I welcomed him as the new "boss" and have never had a finer one.

Another colleague was Dr. Elisha Seujit Tikasingh, a young man of East Indian descent. His father had come to Trinidad as an indentured laborer and later became a Christian minister. Elisha was anomalous among his peers in developing an interest in science. Scholarships and grants took him eventually to the United States where he achieved a Ph.D. in parasitology and then actually studied king crabs in Alaska with the U.S. Fish and Wildlife Service for a year. So few Trinidadians undertake biological careers that Elisha had to be lured back. When he joined TRVL, he didn't know a virus from a sea gull, so he was put to work on mosquitoes.

In addition the lab constantly welcomed many scholars on a temporary basis. These people, who greatly enriched our society, remained for periods of three months up to a year or more, coming from places like Venezuela, Surinam, Jamaica, British Guiana, Argentina, Canada, the United States and England. Then there were also streams of visitors who came for only a few hours or days to peer over our shoulders. Sometimes these were our bosses from New York and London. That makes you very cautious, as the eyes can be felt boring in from behind.

For much of its first decade, TRVL was concerned almost exclusively with arthropod-borne viruses, that is, the class of viruses carried by arthropods—jointed-legged invertebrates embracing a diversity of forms from shrimps and crabs to spiders and flies. Arthropods that carry such viruses are confined principally to mosquitoes and ticks, though sand flies come into the act here and there. The term "arthropod-borne virus" has been shortened conveniently to "arbovirus."

The most famous arbovirus is the one causing yellow fever. During the 1930's the Rockefeller Foundation carried out extensive studies of this disease in South America and Africa, establishing the fact that it is an infection primarily of monkeys in the jungle. Satisfied at last that the yellow fever story had been completed adequately, the Foundation turned to other fields. But some people remained uneasy. During the yellow fever work, other arboviruses were encountered. No one knew what these were, but they were simply dismissed at that time. In the early 1950's the Foundation decided to resume looking at these obscure viruses on a global basis and forthwith set up a series of laboratories in such widely separated places as India, South Africa, Brazil, Trinidad and California. At present some hundred and fifty or more viruses have been named. Thirty-odd arboviruses have been encountered in Trinidad alone, many of these having been discovered there for the first time, though some are now known to occur thousands of miles away.

Naturally the Rockefeller Foundation and other organizations supporting research in arbovirology are interested in improving public health. Well, if the viruses weren't even known, who could say that they did any harm? This was indeed the big gamble at the beginning, but the hunch has paid off. Though no killer of yellow fever's stature was found, an ample number of the "new" viruses have been shown to cause serious and widespread illness or disability in both human beings and livestock.

If you have no assurance that viruses are about, it is discouraging to begin searching for them. But that is what hunters and fishermen do—they hope, and duly set out on a tramp or bait their hooks. Weeks or months of blank results are no deterrent. And at last a day may arrive when the chase is rewarded. Virologists must be sublimated sportsmen, for they go about their tasks with similar undismayed zeal.

Viruses can only rarely be isolated from wild animals directly. That is because they circulate in the blood for only a short time. A mosquito, having acquired a virus while feeding on a vertebrate host, continues to carry the agent for the rest of its life. On the other hand a rat or a robin, infected by the bite of a mosquito, becomes immune within a few days and thereafter removes circulating virus from the blood vessels by means of the developed antibodies. Only during the early period of viremia, when viruses can flow in the blood stream without hindrance, is it possible for a feeding proboscis to suck them up or for a virologist to secure them with a syringe.

Now we begin to approach the reason for my being in Trinidad. Obviously if the lab discovered one new virus after another, and all these viruses came from somewhere out of doors, the next thing to learn is where they reside in nature. One man cannot be a complete virus-investigating team in himself, though a few such as Wil Downs come close to it; the venture requires specialized knowledge in too many fields. Our lab people, for instance, might be the most splendid virologists and serologists, but if they were unable to distinguish one kind of bird or mosquito from another, no sane scientist would dream of criticizing them for ineptitude. Likewise an entomologist could give outstanding service to a virus lab without knowing what goes on in the test tubes. When the scientific report of a new virus is written, the account must include a complete story—not just the biochemical attributes of the virus but as much of its natural history and prevalence as possible. Hence a team is virtually a necessity.

Tommy Aitken being already in charge of entomology, I cast about for unoccupied provinces and adopted birds and small mammals as pets. After all, these are as important as mosquitoes, for the two must play a viral duet. And apart from isolations of viruses themselves, field collections have further contributions to make. Once a virus has been isolated and identified, it is possible to make a kind of reverse investigation into its natural activity.

When birds and mammals pass the stage of viremia—when they no longer circulate viruses in the peripheral blood stream—they have become immune. Their blood then contains various antibodies that can be recognized in the laboratory by a number of tests. Some of the reactions are highly specific, others more general, but they are classified as complement-fixing, hemagglutinating, or neutralizing reactions, each presumably the result of a special kind of antibody. The very multiplicity of antibodies thus far discovered attests to the variety of ways in which vertebrate organisms combat infection, to resist not only viruses but such other invaders as bacteria, worms and ragweed pollen.

The fact that laboratory tests can discriminate between one kind of antibody and another makes it far more profitable to go searching for antibodies than for viruses in wild animals. Thus one can easily make antibody surveys to determine the past distribution of known viruses in populations of all kinds of creatures—human beings, domestic animals including chickens, wild birds, and everything from rats to lizards.

A field naturalist on an arbovirus team consequently does at least two things, these being somewhat in conflict with each other. First he desires to study the habits of the local wildlife, a difficult task that yields best results when the wildlife is disturbed as little as possible. At the same time he wishes to capture his subjects to obtain blood specimens from them, which must be greatly disturbing! Ideally he will divide his terrain into two parts, conducting the opposed types of study independently. When that is not feasible, he must do the best he can not to become schizophrenic in a single location.

The Golden-headed Manakin I mentioned earlier has been held in my hand too long. With an alcohol sponge I wet down the feathers on the right side of the neck and part them until I can see the jugular vein. Light pressure by my left thumb causes the vein to stand out. The narrow-gauge needle slips in easily, and I draw on the plunger until the fluid column stands at 0.1 milliliter, about two ordinary drops. Micromethods in serology and virology have been so refined that this quantity will yield enough material for both the 1,000-to-1 shot at virus itself and for several antibody tests.

Withdrawing the needle, I move my left thumb to the tiny wound and press gently again in case there were any tendency toward hemorrhage. Now I examine the bird's legs. Yes, it is an old friend, for the numbered band it wears was affixed six months ago. My record book quickly informs me that this is the third time the manakin has been bled. How has it been faring? It is a male, sparrow-sized, with jet-black body, orange head, china-white eyes and scarlet and white leggings. Everything about it is sleek, alert, vibrant. My guess is that it is doing very well.

I shall have more to say about my role at TRVL, now that the manakin has flown, but much more about what was not my direct role. Any field naturalist who confines himself to the assigned aspects of an arbovirology program is not only a fool but also a detriment to the lab. That is because of serendipity: I have neglected to remark that *the natural history of not a single arbovirus is fully known.* Consequently many of the things I observed and enjoyed as side lines in Trinidad could have been important to someone else, though as yet none of them has. But I did not regard them from that standpoint. At the time I simply found them as fully absorbing as matters that were tied up with our formal program. Moreover, I was not constrained to say anything about them in annual reports or scientific publications, so they had nothing to do with pay checks—or mental checks, for that matter. These were unrecorded bonuses, as often as not wearing no feathers or fur at all, and I was free to speculate and to appreciate them without stint.

Chapter 2

TROPICAL HOUSEKEEPING

A naturalist should live, eat and sleep among the creatures he is studying. In South Africa I used to stay for months on end at our field station in the Ndumu Game Reserve in northeastern Natal, touching base at the lab in Johannesburg as briefly and infrequently as possible. Imagine my alarm on reaching Trinidad to learn that TRVL maintained no field headquarters. Wil explained that the island is so small—only thirty by fifty miles in extent—that one could easily reach any part of it on a day's expedition and be home in time for dinner and a civilized night's sleep in one's proper bed. But that meant spending only a few hours in the study area—and always the same hours of the twenty-four at that. How can you judge a bit of ground if you never walk it at midnight?

I began needling everybody for at least a hut in the jungle. My colleagues had just discovered a hotbed of arboviruses in Bush Bush Forest, a slightly elevated strip of land in the middle of Nariva Swamp on the eastern side of Trinidad. Wouldn't this be a grand place to set up satellite housekeeping?

My views were regarded as amusing, but that did not silence me. Before long I prevailed on Leslie to take them seriously. He, being strongly gregarious, knew everyone in Port-of-Spain and saw every-

one constantly at every kind of social affair. One morning at our coffee hour he said that he had been told of a small prefabricated house that TRVL could buy cheaply. Our carpenters could disassemble it and then re-erect it in Bush Bush.

I named it "We House." At that time the Canadian government had just presented Trinidad with two ships—the *Federal Palm* and the *Federal Maple*—for inter-island transport. At a dedication ceremony in Port-of-Spain harbor, official dignitaries boarded one of the ships for a celebration. When numerous poor "nonofficial" Trinidadians also attempted to board, they were rudely turned away. "But this is *we ship*," they clamored. That is how We House got its name.

Meanwhile I had met Leon. He worked as occasional yardman, though I learned that he had been a taxi driver who had almost destroyed himself in an accident. (He was lucky: many of them do a complete job.) My criterion of the perfect life at a field station includes the services of a cook. Even if one is only warming up a can of beans, it is necessary to be free to run after a rare butterfly that just flew past, and someone must be on hand to prevent the pot from burning if the chase is long. Though a Trinidadian, Leon was a "city boy," and the hinterlands of his small island were to him dangerously mysterious, peopled by vampires known as "soucouyants" and other terrors. Yet Leon possessed a rudiment of natural curiosity, and the prospect of working for me in a jungle overcame his normal reluctance. At first he read his Bible faithfully. But eventually he neglected the Book in favor of being allowed to set traps for rodents and erect beehives—after he had seen me whitewash the fence enough times. And he could cook. As for what he cooked and how he did it, I'll defer comment.

We made a clearing on Bush Bush Island by taking down as few trees as possible and then making a cement floor about twenty feet square. The asbestos wall panels, bolted to perforated angle-iron girders and topped with corrugated asbestos roofing sheets, combined to make a snug hidey-hole. Rain gutters were arranged to collect water into two 400-gallon tanks, from which pipes led to a tap at the kitchen sink. An outdoor shower was rigged by mounting an oil drum on further struts; the drum could be filled by a hand pump connected to the reservoir tanks.

One thing I vetoed was a gasoline generator for electric power— that was the only complaint I had had at Ndumu. Bam, bam, bam! Sure, we could write our notes there by a flickering bulb at night, but what about all the normal night sounds—insects, frogs, owls? No, a kerosene lamp at We House would be just fine.

We had a kerosene refrigerator, too. At first Leon cooked on a tiny kerosene stove, but it kept getting clogged up and we ultimately shifted to one run by gas which was available in containers light enough to be carried by one struggling man (Leon). The single nonmechanized appurtenance was our outhouse, which I shall eulogize later.

The interior of We House was divided into a dormitory and a working-eating area. The latter was dominated by a very long laboratory bench, salvaged from TRVL's original quarters in the army barracks. I don't know how many times Leon painted that bench— I remember its White Period (which didn't last long) and a later Green Period (when he had some roofing paint left over). Anyhow we lived and labored on the bench, pushing notes and specimens aside for food and vice versa.

Other relics from the old lab included an office swivel chair which I occupied on the "gallery"—a Trinidadian term denoting a porch or veranda. When mosquitoes were not too thick, I could sit comfortably for hours, watching events in the clearing and at the forest's edge. Even indoors the jungle was with us, for two sides of We House were broadly screened. At night in bed we could hear the Atlantic surf, the roar of planes taking off from Piarco Airport to westward in the interior, and the smallest cricket a few yards away.

Also vicious winds and crashing trees. One summer, when I was home on leave, a dead branch was wrenched from a huge overhanging gommier tree and punched a hole in the asbestos roof. Tommy had the tree cut down, to my dismay, rather than simply "tree-surgeoned"; trees are cheap in Bush Bush. But this one was a favorite of Amazon Parrots, and Leon and I were often awakened by a popping shower of discarded fruit dropped by the birds. Since one of Leon's self-appointed chores was to sweep the roof, I think he regretted the gommier's fall less than I.

My house in Port-of-Spain was remarkable chiefly for the poor design of its bathing and toilet facilities. Compared with the outhouse in Bush Bush, however, it was elegant; Tommy writes me that after I left Trinidad it became the Colombian consulate. Since I was now a sole human occupant, I gave Leon orders not to clean it except under my direction, for I was keen to learn what other tenants would do if undisturbed by brooms. I did not actually invite cockroaches by putting food out for them, and I did use a mosquito net at night. But generally I allowed life to take its course, especially spiders, of which eventually I had hundreds.

I was far more interested in the small yard. My landlady gave me permission to dig up a small area in the back to plant vegetables. Rather, she said I could do anything I liked but at the same time suggested that perhaps I would consent to retain Ram Persad, her faithful old East Indian gardener.

Ram Persad and I at once formed a solid though uneasy bond. He hated vegetables but also felt devoted to service; thus I imposed a conflict on him from the very beginning. He carried out my vegetable orders to the least of his conscientious abilities, meanwhile maintaining the lawn and some miserable flowers at their highest possible zenith. I must say that the grass was always beautifully mowed and edged. At times I would find a "volunteer" weed or tree seedling that I wanted to study. "Ram Persad," I would order, "don't disturb that plant." If his adoring eyes could speak, they would have said, "What shocking taste!" I raised his paltry salary from three to four Trinidadian dollars (about U.S. sixty cents each) per week, but Leon informed me later that this made no real difference to Ram Persad, who was a bachelor and lived with kin. The Ugly American could not buy this admirable man, and he continued to regard the garden and my innovations with his own saintly prejudices.

Almost equally as impregnable a fixture in the yard as Ram Persad was the avocado tree. This creation towered its small height over the corrugated iron roof outside my study, giving shade in the afternoons and food for contemplation at all seasons. Never before had I been able to observe how avocados live from year to year. One can easily travel to avocado realms as a tourist and then boast of having seen groves of such trees. But I object twice: a glimpse is fleeting and a grove is not intimate. Give me a single tree and at least a couple of years, and I'll have something inside my head.

The "study" was one of the unused bedrooms. Actually there was another unused one that was nothing at all during my tenure. I occupied what must have been the master bedroom and beyond that was a long room at the front that served as an unpartitioned living-dining room. A spacious kitchen completed the design, except that a carport ("breezeway," I think they call it in the U.S.A.) separated the house from a servant's annex. This was a tiny cubbyhole with cold running water (hot and cold in the home), a toilet with no seat and a shower with no sprinkler head. Here Leon lived and loved with a sense of luxury.

I gather that Leon was born about thirty years ago, somewhere not far out of San Fernando, some twenty or thirty miles south of Port-of-Spain. His parents may have been married, although this is not likely. At least he knew who his mother was, and referred often to the man whom he thought was his father, a shoemaker who gave Leon several of his many useful arts. He was probably correct in recognizing his father, because unmarried couples in Trinidad "go steady" for long periods—sometimes for life—and are just as jealous of infidelities as if they were legally bound to one another.

It is merely convenient not to be tied otherwise. Leon's history, for example, began with a smart girl who produced two sons for him and then obtained a scholarship to study nursing overseas. Something happened. She became pregnant and was shipped back before completing the nursing course. Leon was incensed (for one or another reason) and dropped her cold, though he continued to contribute to the support of his two little boys whenever he had any money.

That was just before I employed him. Being on the loose, he was besieged by women. As often seems to happen, he was the more attractive to them because he is small, both short and slight. The larger women chased after him. Soon he engaged a huge laundress for me, unmarried and with two little daughters of her own. At this juncture Leon began to have thoughts of actual marriage. But there are unwritten requisites in Trinidad about such things. First, you must have a house. Second, you are bound to be able to afford a fine wedding dress for the bride. At least that is what they say, and it must be true, for many weddings are on record at which even grandchildren were on hand to kiss the bride and groom.

During the washerwoman stage Leon approached me for a loan of Tr. $400 to buy a house. "I have a rule not to lend money to employees," I told him.

"You can take fifty dullars out of my salary every month," he said.

That would give him little to live on, but actually he was living on my food and shelter already. I thought of devious plans that might be in his mind. Perhaps he would abscond with the four hundred "dullars" next day. Instead, it was his girl who absconded, in a sense. I lent the money, he bought the house, and when she was six months pregnant, they had a disagreement. To settle matters, she accepted the house as compensation for her swollen uterus. Everyone was happy, I recovered my money from salary withholding and Leon was again on the loose, soon harboring other panting females in his squalid annex—among them a cute small one whom he also considered marrying for a time. Maybe he has.

One day he came in with rum practically spouting from his eyes. "I'm a fader again—anudder boy!"

"Which one?" I asked, forgetting to scold him for absenteeism.

"De laundress, of course."

Chapter 3

LAB AND FIELD CREWS

I have not yet given credit to some fifty additional persons who derived their livelihood directly from the existence of TRVL. I shall not name them all—in fact I am unable to, and on several occasions Tommy was enraged because I could not address an employee by name whom I had known well for four years. Carelessness, deafness—call it what you will: I simply do not remember names of people, though Latin terminology for birds and insects sticks to my mind like a magnet.

At the lab I did not deal with many of these people, who were mainly concentrated there since our field staff was much smaller. The ones with whom I had close contact naturally became dear friends. With the exception of Arthur Green, an Englishman assigned to TRVL as head laboratory technician, all were Trinidadians —East Indians, Spanish, pure African, or Afro-Caucasian "Creoles" as they call themselves. We had one Chinese, too. Their names were usually indicative of racial origins. Thus one can guess the blood lines of Mr. Mohammed, our storekeeper, Joe Hing-Wan, the mosquito expert in the entomology department, Owen Olivier, our chief bird bleeder, and Bertie Sam, my animal attendant.

Bertie was my mainstay in the wild rodent colonies. After I had domesticated some rats from Bush Bush Forest and learned how to breed them, I turned the project over to his responsible hands. It is a tribute not only to Bertie's industry but to his intelligence that the colonies were successful, for they were tricky animals to handle and required someone who would dedicate himself to the extent that he could perceive what was happening and make adjustments accordingly. Many times he reported useful observations that enabled us to improve our procedures or perhaps avert catastrophes.

Bertie was originally a cabinetmaker, but Trinidad being poor, and unemployment being what it is there, the day came when he applied to TRVL for the mundane job of cleaning animal cages. He worked up one notch to the post of animal attendant, which meant that he fed and watered multitudes of mice, hamsters, guinea pigs and rabbits—and someone else cleaned up. From the lab's standpoint, however, these are both highly fundamental posts, for much of the work depends on the maintenance of healthy, fertile animals.

Yet Bertie still could have done a worthwhile job with his brain turned off, simply by following an automatic routine. He wasn't that kind, and hence my satisfaction in him. Indeed his brain was always very much turned on. He was a great politician, often the center of loud discussions during lunch hour, if they weren't playing cricket under the devil's-ear tree. I imagine he was a local orator in his community, since he had somehow developed a large and fluent vocabulary almost devoid of the Trinidadian accent and colloquialisms. If the lab personnel wanted to present a petition to the Director, Bertie Sam was more often than not elected to be their spokesman. And when a farewell party for me was planned, Bertie insisted that it be held at his home. Of course he gave a beautiful speech.

Many of our lab people began as glassware washers. From here the ladder led toward the use of such equipment. When I was in Trinidad, practically all the routine serological tests and mouse inoculations were being set up and performed by individuals who had learned everything they knew about virology within TRVL's walls. Thus Leslie and Dries could simply order work to be done and later inspect the results.

Entomological technicians were in a separate class. We used to deplore the fact that they were not more versatile, but it really took all their time to identify specimens from the field and to main-tain several colonies of mosquitoes and other arthropods. A recruit in this department was taught what to do and then did nothing else. In the rainy season, one might find Raymond Manuel, Raymond Martinez and Joe Hing-Wan sorting mosquitoes all day long, and even Tommy had to pitch in sometimes. To put in order a row of jars, each one containing several hundred mosquitoes of two dozen or more species, is a formidable day's work.

It is essential to separate the mosquitoes into species lots and then either inoculate them or freeze them on the day they come in. This is because any viruses they may contain will be lost if the specimens dry out and also because, if a virus is recovered, one must know from which kind of mosquito it came. And great numbers of mosquitoes are necessary to keep the lab busy, for at times the rate of infection is extremely low—perhaps only one virus carrier in five or ten thousand mosquitoes—or even less in some seasons. Tommy took great pride in the fact that at the latest count well over a million mosquitoes had been identified, ground up and inoculated into mice at TRVL.

Our field staff consisted of two categories—or three, if you con-sider James Thomas in a class by himself. Actually James was desig-nated as the head field man, but he did not spend much time super-vising the others. Somehow there usually seemed to be things that he could do alone, while his crew went about the routine of collecting arthropods.

Wil Downs found James soon after TRVL was established and became much attached to him. They had traits in common, both being vigorous outdoorsmen. I think they used to try to outdo each other on strenuous field excursions, for there are tales of their wading across Nariva Swamp up to their necks in muck and water, holding their guns over their heads to keep them dry. Neither had the nerve to suggest calling it off.

James is still a singularly powerful person. When it comes to fighting bush fires in the dry season or clearing trails of large fallen trees, he can do more than two ordinary men. Yet he enjoys relaxa-tion as well as anybody and always welcomes the time of year when we must clean out the boat line, a shallow ditch leading across the swamp to Bush Bush Island. It is then ludicrous to see him supervising the two or three temporary laborers hired for the job. There he sits on the bank, daintily shading himself with a broad banana leaf!

The five insect collectors were picked up at various places early in the morning and then driven to fixed destinations, depending on the season and the current program. At times they concentrated on Bush Bush Island; otherwise they might work in other parts of Trinidad. Tommy had a routine for each of them so that on any given day one or more men would catch mosquitoes, others search for mosquito larvae, or some might drag flannel flags along the ground and over low vegetation for ticks. These activities accounted for the flow of material received at TRVL. I was going to say that the field collectors were therefore basic to the program, but they are not more so than the rest of the outfit—in a team or a machine you can't single out the one man or part that makes it go.

This essential work went on routinely through the year. To me it seemed very stultifying, and I imagine the job must have become tedious to the collectors. They were solitary sorts. If I met one of them in the woods, we would exchange only a few words before he continued on his way, sweeping a net or dragging a cloth. I did not get to know them well; nor could I name the two big stolid ones, although one of them was James Thomas' cousin.

One aspect of our field work required a resident staff on Bush Bush Island. Here we maintained regular trapping schedules including both rodent collecting and the exposure of sentinel baby mice either in the open or in cages that would retain entering mosquitoes. Those phases of the work were carried out by Moon Jury and his multitudinous family, beginning with his oldest son, Motilal, aged about thirty, and going down through Mohan and Chitram so far as regulars are concerned. One never knew whom one would find at Moon's shack where the boat line reached the island, for whenever he went home he returned one batch of children to Plum Mitan and then came back with another. If the latest baby were included, Mrs. Jury would come along. Altogether this couple had had nineteen children, of whom fourteen were living.

Moon was a tall, thin, handsome East Indian who had practically grown up in Nariva Swamp and its forests. As a youth he had been a keen hunter, preferring to stalk game on moonlight nights. This led to his current nickname, and everyone had forgotten what his real name is.

It is somewhat peculiar—at least remarkable—that the East Indians, who were brought to Trinidad as indentured laborers, have largely clung to bucolic ways, while the descendants of liberated African slaves are more attracted to urban life. Moon typified his people in having progressed from hunter to woodcutter rather than politician. Many East Indians are still Hindus, and they are much more likely to refrain from mixed marriages than other segments of the Trinidadian population. The younger generation is beginning to lose interest in the old ways, but Moon, though born in Trinidad, can speak and read Hindi, a source of amazement to Dr. T. Ramachandra Rao of Poona, India, whom I took to Bush Bush one day.

As a woodcutter, Moon learned every inch of the island. In fact it was he who cut the original shallow boat line in order to float or drag his logs across the swamp to the road. When TRVL decided to investigate viruses in Bush Bush Forest, it was natural to employ Moon as custodian. We impressed on him that there must be no more hunting from now on, for every mammal and bird henceforth had importance for our work. Not that we intended to collect them all— we wanted a natural relationship to exist between vertebrates and arthropods, and selective hunting of a few species could alter normal balances. A ban was put on guns, though at times I suspected that Moon had one concealed somewhere.

Motilal and Leon formed an immediate bond, an example of the interracial amiability that is Trinidad's greatest hope. Mohan was at first an engaging mid-teenager, but by the time I left he had found a lovely little East Indian girl named Toy and could hardly find even minutes to tend to his work. Chitram gave promise of becoming tall and handsome like his father, and the younger ones were still amorphous, dressed in shirts that barely hid their navels. Correction: the little girls sported ragged lace panties. At no time did I see signs of Moon's wanting any of them to grow into something "better" than he. I believe he found a complete life in the swamp and in his own ways.

Chapter 4

NARIVA SWAMP
AND BUSH BUSH ISLAND

To reach the field station in Bush Bush, one first drives east of Port-of-Spain along the Churchill-Roosevelt Highway, the road the air tourist takes into town from Piarco Airport. It is an exhilarating ride. To the north is an undulating range of forested hills, rising to 3000 feet. These small mountains—the Northern Range—are intersected by more than a dozen valleys, some of them traversed by asphalt roads, others only by donkey trails. Much of the precipitous land is clothed in original forest: someone's forefathers in Trinidad were wise enough to realize that uninhibited cutting of timber would lead to irreparable erosion and a future desert.

The plain along the highway is fertile and well-watered by seasonal inundations, irrigation being rarely necessary. Near Port-of-Spain, East Indians toil in truck gardens throughout the year, raising tomatoes, corn, eggplant, okra and other vegetables during the dry season and converting the same plots to rice paddies when the land is flooded. Farther away the acreage is devoted to sugar cane. Here East and West merge as one sees a field being plowed with a tractor, while water buffaloes haul away the recently reaped harvest in wooden carts.

After the turnoff for Piarco (Leon and I are going the opposite direction from the tourist's), the terrain becomes less fertile, with many cocorite palms in evidence. These have been long recognized by the Forestry Department as indicators of poor soil, and new farms are discouraged where they grow. At the same time the Northern Range on our left becomes more rugged and majestically verdant. The road veers southeast to Sangre Grande, the largest town in the eastern half of Trinidad, and then continues through plantations of cocoa, coffee and citrus trees to the coast at Manzanilla. Now for seven or eight miles it parallels the beach. All along the way coconut palms overhang the highway, and I was always afraid that a nut would drop and smash the windshield. They do drop all the time, but I have never heard of such an accident.

The drive takes an hour and three quarters to the beginning of the boat line at the forty-six-mile post. When I first came to Trinidad this was a wilderness, with mangroves, slender spiny palms and mixed swamp-forest hardwood trees lining the road on both sides. Later several East Indian squatters moved in and cleared most of the west side in order to plant melons in the dry season. This was so-called Crown Land. I believe they had no right to it, but on the other hand no one drove them away. I deplored the cutting and burning, for the original setting was more exciting. As one entered the boat and set off to the west, it seemed as if a mysterious land lay ahead. Now one simply waved good-by to the melon planters, knowing that they would still be close at hand. Moon, in fact, welcomed their presence, for he was able to arrange a signal—two shots fired in quick succession—that would notify him in Bush Bush that he was wanted ashore. He called this his "telephone."

Nariva Swamp is five or six miles wide, lying just west of the coastal strip. It is by no means a salt marsh, nor is it permanent. Durng the rainy ,season it receives the runoff from Trinidad's Central Range. Thus fresh water drains into it from the west and gradually seeps out into coastal streams and rivers. Tidal fluctuations bring some salt water into its eastern margin—hence the mangroves that flank the forty-six-mile post.

But the boat does not go far before leaving mangroves behind. Now we enter a zone dominated by tall royal palms, many of which contain large cavities in which Amazon Parrots nest. This belt soon gives way to an open grassy savanna that looks fit to walk on and actually is in years with a pronounced dry season. Most of the time, however, the appearance of solid footing is illusory: under the dense mat of grass there may be several feet of water overlying soft mud. "Alligators," as caymans are popularly called, lurk here; their true dangerousness was soon impressed on me by the fact that as James Thomas sat under his banana leaf watching the diggers, he always kept a loaded gun at hand. Moon, too, was ever alert. There were some parts of the swamp he would refuse to enter. A fisherman shot a six-foot cayman not far from We House—its head was bigger than mine, if somewhat flatter.

Dotted over the savanna are large stands of moriche palms, resembling the "hammocks" of our Everglades. These trees are really palmettos, with broad fan-shaped leaves. They bear long clusters of nuts a bit smaller than tennis balls. The fruits are covered on the outside with a soft red pulp that is greatly favored by Small Red-bellied Macaws. This palm exists also in Venezuela. Many of its nuts fall into the Orinoco and are eventually washed ashore in Trinidad, where the local residents call them "sea coconuts."

Straight ahead lies a wall of moriche palms that is obviously more than an isolated patch. This is the fringe of Bush Bush "island," a swamp-forest border between the savanna and dry land. As one enters this stretch, the sun is quickly blotted out and one winds among buttressed trunks of tall hardwood trees, many of them clad in climbing vines. It is a typical Hollywood movie set, except that it is real. Birds of many kinds flit across the waterway, but one cannot get a good look at them. Now and then a giant blue Morpho butterfly flashes past. The only thing that mars the atmosphere—and this has been true for the whole journey—is the damned outboard motor. What this scene needs is silence, except for the screaming parrots and droning cicadas.

Another bend, and there is Moon's shack. In all we have come about a mile, though the variety of changes in scene makes it seem more than that. If you listen, you can still hear the roar of the surf to the east.

Bush Bush Island is a generally level and sandy bit of land surrounded by swamp. It runs north and south for about four miles,
varying in width from an eighth to a third of a mile, though here
and there it extends longer arms to westward. Its configuration and
composition suggest that this may have been a coastal sand dune
in past geological times. Such undulations as occur in the terrain
amount to no more than a dozen feet.

Except where man has felled trees or made clearings, the area
is solidly forested. Perhaps I should modify that statement to include
the ravages of fires that occasionally sweep across the savanna, encouraged by prevailing easterly winds, and take bites out of the
forest here and there. After such conflagrations the toll of falling
trees continues for years because charring of healthy trunks at ground
level allows slow decay to begin. However these losses are gradual,
and a fallen tree trunk is soon obscured amid hosts of saplings that
take advantage of sudden access to sunlight. Most of the forest has
been spared recent fires—or any at all, so far as I know. It so happened that the region in which We House is situated, near the
northern tip of the island, has been scorched repeatedly in the last
decade. Hence I found a modified habitat at my doorstep and had
to walk several hundred yards to encounter normal situations.

If We House was primitive, Moon's shack could be called only a
hovel. It had a board floor placed on wooden stilts and a palm-
thatched roof. At first there were no walls at all, but when vampire
bats began to annoy sleepers, the lab provided screen doors and
chicken-wire siding. Moon did not particularly object to the blood
lappers, but our concern was for the possibility of rabies infection.
(Incidentally the virus causing hydrophobia is not an arbovirus,
since it is transmitted directly from vertebrate to vertebrate without
an arthropod intermediary.)

It is only a short walk from Moon's shack to We House. Leon and I
carry our stuff there in a few minutes, while Moon or Mohan follow
later if we have brought heavy items such as a case of evaporated
milk or canned peaches. Then, while Leon gets the kerosene refrigerator going, I have a quick run-around to see what has happened
since last visit. Naturally I can't cover everything. So far as that goes,

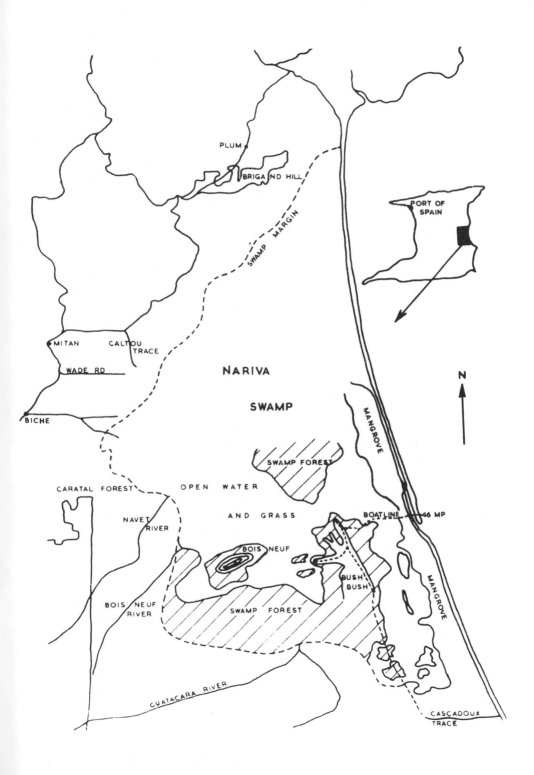

PLUM

BRIGAND HILL

SWAMP MARGIN

PORT OF SPAIN

MITAN   CALTOU
TRACE

WADE RD

NARIVA

BICHE

SWAMP

N

SWAMP FOREST

CARATAL FOREST   OPEN WATER

BOATLINE   46 MP

AND GRASS

MANGROVE

NAVET
RIVER

BOIS   NEUF

BUSH
BUSH

BOIS NEUF
RIVER

SWAMP FOREST

MANGROVE

GUATACARA RIVER

CASCADOUX
TRACE

I never in four years did go much farther south than our one-mile boundary mark. The Forestry Department gave TRVL a kind of authority within that domain. This extended westward along one of the long arms of the island to a locality designated as Big Bush Bush. That was plenty of room for arbovirus studies, but Tommy had larger ideas. Having involved the government to the extent of permitting us to work on Crown Lands, he was—and still is—impelled to persuade them to proclaim this a nature reservation. As everywhere else, the population explosion is threatening primeval wildlife habitats in Trinidad.

I have many favorite trails on the island, some cut by myself with a machete or "cutlass," as they call the weapon in Trinidad, others anciently established by woodcutters and hunters, some possibly by Moon himself. From We House I go first to the nearby incursion of savanna called Petit Bush Bush Swamp, where Tommy had a wooden ramp built over the marsh in order to study mosquito breeding. From here the trail converges with another south of Moon's camp. One then reaches a fork, the left leading south all the way to Cascadoux Trace on the mainland. To the right, one is soon accosted by another divergence: right leads to Big Bush Bush, left to Tommy's tree platforms. At one time Tommy had three of these, erected with builders' scaffolding around the supporting trunks of giant yellow olivier trees. The top platform was at fifty-five feet, and intervening ones occurred at twenty-foot intervals from the ground. Under his direction mosquito catchers sat at the various levels, collecting whatever came to bite. Tommy was thus able to delineate the vertical stratification of various mosquitoes at all seasons and during the twenty-four hours of any day.

The Bush Bush study area was really quite small. I could get out to the farthest point in Big Bush Bush in less than half an hour if I wanted to, though meandering usually stretched the time inordinately. Moon, however, having traps and sentinel animals to service, could make his rounds in short order. The wonder is that in such small compass there *was* such wonder.

Chapter 5

MONKEYS

*W*hat the average visitor to Bush Bush most wants to see—or at least to hear—is a band of red howler monkeys. That gratification can not be guaranteed, for by the time we pick up our guests at a hotel in Port-of-Spain and reach the forty-six-mile post, it is already eight o'clock. The howlers have long since sung their matins. Now there is only a chance that two roving bands will meet and have a midmorning roaring powwow, or that a sudden shower will send them into clamors of protest.

Spending many nights at We House over the years, I became so accustomed to howlers that sometimes I forgot to listen to them in the sense of really appreciating each anguished note and remembering to congratulate myself for being present at every concert. However I remained constantly aware of them in a more general way. For example, if they failed to call on some morning or evening, I would wonder where they had wandered—for it was unthinkable that they would remain silent. And when they did locate themselves, I made a vague mental note as to the number of different bands within earshot and the direction of each one.

This surveillance was part of my duties, and also of Moon's and his sons'. TRVL was vitally interested in howler monkeys, and not just because they entertained distinguished visitors. I have already mentioned monkeys in the jungle yellow fever cycle in South America and Africa. They have played the same role in Trinidad in the past. Rather curiously, they helped put TRVL on the map, for Wil had no sooner got the lab properly set up when an outbreak of yellow fever occurred—a tragedy for the monkey population and a few human beings but a most timely episode for TRVL, provided it had to take place at all.

That was in 1954. In those days the island was still heavily infested with the urban yellow fever mosquito, *Aëdes aegypti*. To recapitulate a fragment of the familiar yellow fever story, the threat that now worried the authorities was the spread of infection from the jungle into towns and cities. This could happen if the following chain of happenings took place in properly synchronized sequence.

Let's begin with a sick monkey in Bush Bush Forest. Or, let's begin with a viremic monkey, for the animal might look healthy. A forest-canopy mosquito of the genus *Haemagogus* bites the monkey, sucking up yellow fever virus with the blood meal. After several days the virus has multiplied in the mosquito and is now teeming in the insect's salivary glands. Now a woodcutter chops down the tree where *Haemagogus* is resting. The disturbed mosquito is ready for its next meal anyhow, so it bites the woodcutter at ground level, injecting an infective dose of virus. The woodcutter finishes his day's work and goes home. Next day, still feeling fine, he decides to visit relatives in Port-of-Spain. He plans to return in a couple of days, but suddenly he comes down with a fever. His kin put him to bed. This is a poor family; their house is unscreened. *Aëdes aegypti* mosquitoes are breeding in and around the house, in water containers of all kinds: flower vases, old tin cans, water barrels, discarded tires, chamber pots, etc. They bite the sickened woodcutter unmercifully, and within several additional days they are prepared to infect other human beings. *Aëdes aegypti* does not fly far, but the houses are close together in this impoverished section of the city. All of a sudden an epidemic erupts locally. Moreover, some of the infected urban residents have also been moving about. During early stages of their viremia, before feeling stricken, they have seeded the virus in mosquitoes in many other parts of Port-of-Spain. Thus when the cycle completes itself a second time, the epidemic is no longer local but more like the havoc of a campfire that has showered sparks in all directions under the influence of a fickle wind. A third cycle, and the entire city is in flames, including the finest residences and best hotels.

Then what happens in a West Indian tourist resort? Yellow fever is much more than a local health problem—it can affect many other countries where *Aëdes aegypti* exists but the virus does not. Returning tourists in early, previremic stages of infection can serve, just as the woodcutter did when he came to town, to begin satellite conflagrations far away. An international quarantine must be imposed. Moreover, tourists no longer want to come to Trinidad. The island not only has to face its own dismal health crisis but essential revenue is lost because outsiders don't feel it is any of their concern to patronize Trinidad at personal risk.

Things are no longer as bad as that. Even in 1954, when TRVL made its first big splash, a splendid immunizing vaccine was available to protect anyone who wished to receive a shot. In those days tourists were still advised to do so, and several campaigns to immunize residents had been undertaken. But the obvious measure to endorse was a program for eliminating *Aëdes aegypti*. If the urban vector were not there, a rare viremic woodcutter from the sticks would not be a hazard in the city. He could visit his relatives, come down with a fever, be bitten by other kinds of household mosquitoes, and die or survive. But that would be the end of it. Only *Aëdes aegypti* can support growth of yellow fever virus outside the jungle.

That, of course, brings up a fascinating problem which occupied much of our thought about other viruses: the nature of host specificity. And this applies to many other parasitic organisms such as protozoa, bacteria and worms. Why, for example, could *Aëdes aegypti* bite the viremic woodcutter and become infected, when the same sick man was riddled by proboscides of ordinary bedroom mosquitoes, *Culex pipiens*, without conferring infection to them? Or why could the *Aëdes aegypti* then infect another man but not a dog or cat under the same roof? At present we can only assert that those are the facts, even though there is no known explanation for them.

Therefore Trinidad, upon strong urging from TRVL, undertook to eradicate *Aëdes aegypti*. This costs a good deal of money but is not as impractical as it may sound. The species, native to Africa, is believed to have been brought to the Americas on slave ships. During those slow journeys on sailing vessels, yellow fever epidemics were perpetuated on board by mosquitoes breeding in water containers and biting chained slaves in the hold. Many a carcass was thrown overboard in mid-ocean, and they weren't always slaves, for yellow fever does not recognize race.

But by good fortune the strain of *Aëdes aegypti* that arrived in the New World had already adapted itself so fully to the ways of man in African settlements that it seemed now unable to spread into forests. Originally it was a "tree-hole" breeder, but the segment of of the population brought to the Western Hemisphere had become addicted not to flooded natural hollows in rotting branches and trunks but to the kinds of water collections that man accumulates about himself in the regular course of his living. *Aëdes aegypti* is still known as an uncommon jungle mosquito in some parts of Africa where human inhabitants are scarce. These representatives must be aboriginal, for they continue to breed in tree holes and seem to be unfamiliar with tin cans, rubber tires, garden urns, rain gutters and floral vases.

Remarkable as it may sound that memory or habit can be genetically ingrained in an ancestral line of a given kind of mosquito, the fact is true: in the New World *Aëdes aegypti* has not yet reverted to tree-hole breeding in any important instance. Control measures can consequently be employed easily by hiring cheap laborers to empty all water containers in homes and public places. The countryside may be largely ignored. Modern insecticides such as DDT, other chlorinated hydrocarbons, or even newer classes of chemicals aid in the attack against both mosquito larvae and flying adults (though the insects may become resistant after generations of such contact). The government of Trinidad therefore had to engage in little more than an urban cleanup and anti-pest campaign.

Fortunately a combination of these measures and further vaccination of the human population averted a significant epidemic in Trinidad in 1954. Before long the quarantine was lifted, and tradesmen and hoteliers resumed their traffic in North American dollars. Since that time anti-*aegypti* control has been rigorously maintained, much to Trinidad's satisfaction and profit a couple of years ago when an epidemic of dengue fever raged in many other Caribbean islands and along the north coast of South America.

The arbovirus causing dengue is another mysterious character, for it has no known vertebrate host other than man. However, it shares with yellow fever virus the capacity to thrive in *Aëdes aegypti* mosquitoes but not in the common *Culex* species. Dengue is not a fatal disease, though at the height of fever, when the patient feels that his very bones are cracking apart, he wishes that he could die. The malady spreads through urban settlements just like yellow fever. Then why were the other islands so lax in their anti-*aegypti* measures? The answer is that they have no native monkey populations. Dengue may come and go, making a lot of people uncomfortable, but it and the *Aëdes* population are no threats to life. Of course it is always possible for a tourist or a seaman to arrive from South America with an incipient infection by yellow fever virus: a day or so later he could infect local mosquitoes. But today this risk is much smaller than it used to be, because most persons who know that they are going to an area where yellow fever is endemic seek vaccination beforehand. Indeed, prior inmmunization is usually a requirement for their permission to re-enter their countries of origin.

Leslie could afford to chuckle when dengue popped up all around but spared Trinidad. He used to own a boat which he cherished dearly, unberthing it on week ends to take his family to their water-front home on nearby Monos Island. Once, while the vessel was tied up on the Trinidad side during the week, conscientious *aegypti* scouts discovered developing larvae in a collection of rain water somewhere on the craft. Leslie, as head of TRVL, followed the only course open to his moral sense: he sold the boat. Never let it be said that the Regional Virus Director had reintroduced *Aëdes aegypti* into Trinidad! The bitterness of the sacrifice was amelorated when Trinidad escaped not only a wave of dengue but also the other consequences that would have followed, were *aegypti* still here. Whereas the other islands were simply held under close observation, Trinidad would again have been quarantined because of those monkeys.

International regulations do not stipulate yellow fever vaccination for tourists visiting Trinidad today, for it is assumed that they will not visit jungles. The mass of them won't, to be sure, but I have mentioned the numbers of ornithologists and other naturalists that have begun to travel to far places. For these, and for TRVL's scientific visitors with interests in Bush Bush Forest, a yellow fever shot is a must.

Wil's strenuous association with James Thomas began during the 1954 episode. When the first case of yellow fever was recognized, Wil decided that the monkey population must be examined. This meant monkey hunts, as well as posting a reward for anyone who could locate sick or dead monkeys. Wil and James shot several agile ones, at great pains to themselves and the animals. Sick ones were hard to come by, for ordinarily a wild creature behaves normally almost up to the time of its demise. One might think that dead monkeys would have no value in virus investigations, but that is not true. In the tropics a carcass is reduced to a skeleton so quickly by scavengers and natural decay that anything still resembling a dead animal, rather than its bony framework, must be fairly fresh. Wil actually recovered yellow fever virus from one specimen that was almost a skeleton but retained a few fragments of tissue clinging to the bones. I believe it was at the foot of the tree where this animal was found that Tommy collected numerous *Haemagogus* mosquitoes that yielded several additional isolations of yellow fever virus.

Why not, then, exterminate monkeys as well as *Aëdes aegypti*? This measure was actually entertained by some people, but the whole problem is not nearly clear enough to justify such a villainous procedure. The yellow fever cycle is extremely obscure during long periods when disease is absent in both monkeys and men. It is likely that primates, with or without tails, are similarly incidental victims when the virus breaks out of its hiding place, and one might just as illogically propose the elimination of mankind as a control measure.

After 1954, howlers were said to have been scarce in Bush Bush Forest. Survivors may have escaped infection or had "light cases." By the time I came on the scene in 1960, they were again abundant, and during the next five years we waited breathlessly for another outbreak. The closest I came to a heart attack was one day when Motilal rushed in from his bird-netting rounds with the report: "I think I see sick monkey in tree." That, if true, would have upset every planned schedule at TRVL. Everyone would have gotten into the game, at the expense of programs already lined out to the last baby mouse. But when I peered with binoculars into a tangle of vines high above the forest floor where Motilal had spotted a brown object resembling a crouched, immobile monkey, I could see that it was only a huge wasps' nest plastered against a branch.

Throughout my tenure there were occasional other alarms. One concerned a "dead monkey" reported to James Thomas by a hunter. We still had rewards ready for any such finds, so we sent James off to recover the reputed remains at a distant point in the Northern Range. The relics of fur and bones proved to be those of a dog. . . . When I left Trinidad in 1965, I had not had occasion to set my sights against monkeys.

Aside from noting howlers when they made their presence known, we did not further any special studies of them in Bush Bush Forest. Our attention was directed to other animals by other viruses. Yet often while traversing the forest on some mission I would suddenly become aware of being beneath a band of silent monkeys. Perhaps a fruit seed would strike the ground or a small branch would snap overhead. Then I would gradually pick them out one by one as they gave themselves away by reaching for a leaf or simply scratching. They had not attempted to be secretive or to maintain concealment: they were merely unconcerned, not having been shot

at in Bush Bush for many years. But during periods when they are nonvocal and devoted to quiet feeding, they can easily be missed. I have no doubt that I frequently passed below howler bands without knowing it.

When the animals saw me gazing at them through binoculars, they would sometimes become uneasy, though if they were in an especially high tree it did not bother them. If they felt disturbed, they would interrupt their feeding and peer intently at me, moving their heads from side to side and grimacing. Occasionally a male would give a few short growls, but not the full-throated, prolonged howl with which he would have challenged a rival band. This might have been a sort of threat, though it more resembled a combination of curiosity with a hint of undefined fear. If I remained on the spot, the band would quietly move a bit farther out of range, deliberately making up their minds one by one to follow the first retreating animal.

The "howl" of a red howler is not always given in full. From the sound of the preliminaries, I gather that a mature male has to work himself up to a pitch before he can give out the stereotyped performance, and sometimes he abandons it, as if the whole thing is too much trouble. But once he passes a certain point the sequence seems to become involuntary—I doubt that he could stop if he wanted to. His first notes comprise a series of coughs, irregularly spaced, as if he were clearing his throat or simply testing out his own mood. Then the coughs become more resonant as vocalization is added. These mount to rapidly succeeding roars—from now on the final prolonged groans are inevitable. The lamentations, which gradually diminish, are loudest of all, carrying through forest and across savanna for at least a mile. They have a sort of sobbing quality which might indicate despair or ineffable rage. A person unfamiliar with howler monkeys but aware of jaguars would certainly be terrified on first hearing them; I know *I* was in Honduras in 1930.

Who can tell? Perhaps the animals are only expressing joy in the one way open to them. There can't be that much woe each morning as a howler wakes to confront another day. And when two bands meet and exchange howls, they apparently are not preparing for warfare but only saluting each other. In Panama, at any rate, the monkeys have been observed to exchange what could be threats or mere conversation—but never blows—before retiring in peace.

Undoubtedly the howlers in Bush Bush had definite ranges or territories, for this characteristic of monkey bands has been documented also on Barro Colorado Island in Panama. Here, however, I was never able to pin down any such delimitation. We knew that some bands at times crossed the open savanna, for we would encounter monkeys in trees completely surrounded by open terrain near the boat line. To me it seemed that they wandered aimlessly. On the other hand James Thomas and Moon Jury assured me that howlers recognize certain centers to which they retreat to defecate. The men called these "latrine trees." One such tree stood at the south end of Petit Bush Bush Swamp, and the ground beneath it sometimes attested to that practice.

My enjoyment of howlers was greatest when they would come to visit me at We House. I did much of my work on the small gallery out of doors. Here I would sit in a swivel chair alongside my work table, with binoculars in easy reach. Whenever I looked up, I would be confronted by the wall of forest surrounding our small clearing. A lone cocorite palm was the only tree left standing in the open— all else was a looming perimeter of trunks and lofty branches: matchwoods, mahoes, cecropias, "forked-sticks," guatecares, hog plums, yellow oliviers and a host of others that I never learned.

In late afternoons a band of howlers sometimes passed among these trees along an aerial roadway that they knew, for they always used the same route. Their progress was dilatory. Perhaps I had not seen the first monkey go by, but once aware of the visitation, I would stop what I was doing to count those I could see. Again and again I would think that the last one had come and gone, but then another idler would appear. Within the masses of foliage they were often perceptible only as monkeys. However in a few places they were forced to expose themselves, especially where they made a traverse from one tree to another whose branches barely met. An average group of eight to ten individuals might consist of two males, distinguished by their larger size, swollen throats where the hollow hyoid bone lent them their resonant howling ability, and long beards; four or five females; and a number of young. On sunny days the animals sometimes looked bright red.

Occasions of this sort allowed me to gaze at the monkeys without alarming them. They might even find a suitable feeding tree nearby and pause for an hour or so to pluck leaves. Then I would say to Leon, "It's getting late, and they're still there. Maybe they'll decide to spend the night. Then tomorrow morning we'll have a real concert right outside the window." But they never did. At some time they would move silently away, and tomorrow's *aubade* might be half a mile distant.

Cebus monkeys—the familiar capuchin companions of organ-grinders—also inhabit Trinidad, though I knew of only one band on Bush Bush Island. Of course they only chatter and squeal; if they could howl, one might be more aware of them. This band could often be found south of Petit Bush Bush Swamp, near the mosquito-catching tree platforms. Again, however, the animals were known to travel for considerable distances. They visited We House on a few occasions, and Wil told me that when he and James were shooting monkeys, they sometimes bagged a cebus that was pierced by the long spines of slender palms that grow only along the swamp edge. Moon and James called these "white monkeys." My impression is that they were more shy than howlers, for even if I succeeded in getting directly below the cebus band, the individuals retired more quickly than howlers and kept as much out of sight as possible while doing so.

Organ-grinders' monkeys seem healthy enough as they collect pennies and tip their hats. Why are they always capuchins? Apparently they are omnivorous, while the howler is adapted to a diet of certain leaves that cannot be duplicated in captivity. For this reason howlers are only rarely and briefly exhibited even in zoos, where diets can be scientifically prepared. But occasional exceptions occur. Wil Downs had a captive red howler for something like seven years, and it was still well when he had to leave Trinidad and abandon it. When I asked him what he felt had accounted for

such longevity, he said he didn't feel, he *knew*. They began feeding
the howler on all sorts of table scraps, to see if it showed any
preferences. One day some child or other who didn't like tapioca
pudding for dessert slipped it to the monkey. Slurp! It was gone in
a flash. Thereafter the howler received tapioca pudding every day
of its long life. This seems to me a far cry from tropical forest-
canopy leaves, but the proof was surely in that pudding.

Bush Bush visitors were usually screened for their genuine interest in our work. Rarely was it necessary to conduct people about the
forest for purely social or political reasons. Often these persons
were as bored by it all as we were. Maddeningly enough, howlers
almost always put on a show on those dull days—brazenly—while
behaving as if extinct when "big shots" were on hand. Perhaps
they know something that I have missed.

Chapter 6

SMALL MAMMALS

*W*ays of catching mice are traditional insofar as there are always new methods. For that matter, zoologists are unable to say where a mouse ends and a rat begins, making the entire business more evanescent than one would suspect at first. No convenient vernacular word to embrace both rats and mice exists, for the term "rodent" includes innumerable unlikely kin such as squirrels, muskrats, beavers, and guinea pigs. But not rabbits! These are set apart, despite their rasping incisor teeth, as more closely related to deer.

The most convenient term to use, if one is referring not to elephants or tigers but to lesser four-footed furry creatures, is "small mammal." I had a hard time training my Trinidad colleagues in that terminology, for they insisted on calling every such creature a rodent. After all, we had murine opossums in Bush Bush Forest, and these are relatives of kangaroos. (But my friends weren't as far afield as the majority of mankind who use expressions like "animals and birds" or "animals and men," as if animals are restricted to quadrupedal mammals. An animal is of course any living thing that is not a plant. Players of the old game of Twenty Questions had it right when they divided the material universe into three primary categories: Animal, Vegetable and Mineral.)

One has a choice of several ways to trap, depending on what

one's purposes are. The simplest traps are those which kill as well as catch. If extermination is the goal, these are fine. They are suitable also in zoological studies directed simply at establishing the kinds and numbers of small mammals in a given environment at a particular time. However, almost all of our work in Bush Bush Forest demanded living specimens. The ones that Moon Jury caught south of the We House area were shipped to the lab, where they could be bled from the heart and then sacrificed for attempts at virus isolation from organ suspensions inoculated into experimental animals. You can't bleed a dead animal, for the blood has not only ceased to flow but it eventually clots in the vessels. The northern tip of Bush Bush Island, extending from We House, was my "nonremoval" province, in which I trapped, marked and released small mammals in hope of retrapping and recognizing them in the future. In this instance I realized the medical zoologist's ideal, our Bush Bush terrain being extensive enough to satisfy both the lab's demands and my own.

"Live" traps also come in many designs. Some are shockingly inhumane—the others inhumane, perhaps, but not shockingly so. One knows what bear traps are like, with their powerful toothed steel jaws; and one has read of foxes that chew off their own feet to escape such death grips. When it comes to small mammals, that design is not efficient, thank goodness, and the alternative to a snap trap is one that will confine the intact animal in a box or cage. This means that the device must be equipped with a trigger that will close a door when the creature has entered to feed on an appropriately selected bait. After testing several such traps in Trinidad, we learned that the most effective one in that tropical latitude was the well-named Hav-a-hart. This ingenious trap actually has two doors, one at either end, so that even a timorous animal might feel confident in entering it: from the point of ingress it can see what looks like a convenient exit straight ahead. Alas! the treacherously unstable bait treadle halfway through trips both front and back doors with a clang.

What is a mouse or rat or murine opossum to do after the clash? A long night may still remain ahead. When he makes his trapping rounds in the morning, a zoologist can often discern evidence of continuing industry or self-interest in his captives. The first response seems to be gastronomic: few animals are so upset that they will not finish the meal that attracted them in the first place. Next comes the normal desire for escape: much time has been spent in gnawing wire mesh, which here and there gleams nakedly without its usual dull film of metallic oxide. At last resignation: now is the time for shelter and warmth—the animals may pull in such twigs and leaves as they can reach through the half-inch meshes and curl up in a makeshift nest.

But not all is as safe as that, despite the traps' guarantee against attacks by nocturnal snakes and owls. Rarely the zoologist encounters only a stripped carcass swarming with ants. How these insects can appreciate that the trapped mammal is a "sitting duck" for their slaughter and dismemberment, I don't know. And these aren't army ants, either: they are a smaller kind that simply flows into the trap and engulfs large morsels. I like to hope that the animal really died first, as the result of fright or possibly from a blow by one of the clapping doors. Removing remains in this state from traps is one of the zoologist's more unpleasant duties, for he is still bound to make what he can of the specimen, and ants can be venomously resentful of his interference: they quickly overrun him, biting while they bypass hands and shoes to penetrate his clothing painfully. If you see such a naturalist frantically taking down his pants in the jungle, it is not a sure sign that he has diarrhea.

Museum mammalogists habitually utilize ants because of this trait. Having skinned their specimens, they now need cleaned skeletons for complete documentaton of the genus and species. Why not set the carrion on an anthill or place it in an empty can, lid still attached, perforated with holes of a size to admit ants? In a week—two weeks, it does not matter—the skeleton will be ready, its parts remaining in their proper anatomical relationships so that the need for reconstructon is obviated. Ants are always prepared for that task—as I have implied, they are indeed too eager.

It is a shame that small mammals cannot be studied without trapping them. To be sure, a few scientists have rigged up electronic contraptions for photographing them as they pass certain points, but this does not yield much information. One cannot go on a "small mammal walk" and expect to see anything. Most of these beasts are nocturnal and all are secretive. In all the time I spent at Bush Bush, I never saw a mouse or a murine opossum that had not been trapped.

Consequently so few people are familiar with wild rodents that many have no vernacular names—or the names, if any, are used only by mammalogists who would rather use Latin titles anyhow. That's what we did, for once we became used to them, they were actually shorter and more convenient than English ones. The Trinidadian cane rat, for instance, is technically *Zygodontomys brevicauda*, but to us it was simply Zygo. Similarly the terrestrial rice rat, *Oryzomys laticeps*, became simply *Oryzomys* and the spiny pocket mouse, *Heteromys anomalus*, was *Heteromys*. I'll admit this put a strain on Moon and Mohan, for at one period we wanted them to release trapped animals where they were caught but to send us a record of their trapping success. Thus I would receive notes from them such as the following: "2 Headaromea, 1 Oresa Mea, 1 Zy Aromea."

Moon and his peers being such eager hunters, we were astonished at the beginning of our association to learn that these people don't know one rat from another. Their keenness is confined to the quarry they have chased all their lives—larger game such as agoutis, pacas, deer, armadillos and tropical opossums (not the little murine ones). But because of their trained eyes, it was not difficult to teach them. *Oryzomys* is a quite ratty-looking rat, though more sleek and trim than domestic varieties. It is brown with large eyes and ears and a long tail. Zygo is squatter, shorter-tailed, with smaller eyes and ears and a rougher pelage. *Heteromys* is far different: its gray upper fur is sharply demarcated from the white underparts. The eyes appear to be very weak. Although it is called a mouse, it is the same size as Zygo and *Oryzomys*, which are classed as rats. The cheek pouches of *Heteromys* are external, that is, not connected with the mouth cavity; they can be distended with food for transportation, and specimens from the traps were often crammed with peanut butter. The two murine opossums, both belonging to the genus *Marmosa,* of course don't resemble rats at all, once you take a close look at them: the only point of likeness is their size. A widely gaping mouth evenly lined with pointed teeth suggests nothing of gnawing behavior, and the prehensile tail is also extremely un- rodentlike. These animals are brown in general, with black facial masks. Again Moon was astonished when we told him there were two kinds—he had always assumed that smaller ones were merely immature examples of the larger species.

MURINE OPOSSUM

All these animals differed also in their behavior in the traps and when being handled. *Oryzomys* was the most industrious nest- builder; Zygo was the wildest. *Heteromys* and the two marmosas were likely to curl up in a corner and wait. Handle them? This was easy enough. I made my trapping rounds in the morning with a supply of small sacks and stringed labels. Fitting a sack over one of the Hav-a-hart doors, I would open that exit and literally blow the animal into the cloth container. Each sack was then tied shut with the trap location noted on the label so that the specimen could be liberated later in its home territory.

At We House, Leon boiled up a few simple instruments for me, and I immobilized the animals by giving them an intraperitoneal injection of Nembutal. To do this I felt a sack's contents until I located the mammal's head. Then, gripping the body firmly, with the head and neck between thumb and forefinger, I could untie the sack and evert it until the abdomen came into view. A prick of the needle, and I tied up the sack again until the animal went to sleep. Zygos almost invariably struggled the instant they were grasped. At the opposite extreme were *Heteromys* and murine opossums, which remained almost inert. The former response I could understand but not the latter: if a hawk or owl seizes a small mammal, isn't there some hope of escape if it squirms? Why were some of these creatures so meek?

Individual human beings have a greater susceptibility to various chemical substances than other persons. One martini may send Mr. A sky-high while not at all affecting Mr. B, who is exactly the same age and weight. The same was true of Nembutal in my Bush Bush animals. I had to be careful of the "Mr. A" type, for even a small shot put them to sleep permanently. Therefore I always began with very small doses—about half a cc. that contained 2.5 mg. of the drug. When I encountered "Mr. B" I would have to give repeated injections, and even then he might never pass out completely but merely become groggy enough for me to manipulate him.

Now for the documentation. Weight: so many grams. Total length, tail length: so many millimeters (giving an approximate indication of age). Sex. If a male, are the testes in the scrotum? (In young animals they are still intra-abdominal.) If female, can milk be expressed from the nipples, indicating a current litter? Can large embryos be felt through the relaxed abdominal wall, or is nothing of active interest going on at present? What about general nutritional state? Evidence of disease or past injuries? External parasites such as fleas, ticks, mites, lice, botfly larvae?

All these data are rapidly gleaned and entered on a file card. Then it is time for surgery. Rodents have four functional toes on each forefoot and five on the hind ones, giving a total of eighteen digits. Amputation of toes in various combinations permits the identification of thousands of individuals, though the last unfortunate one on the list would be stumping about like a basket case. Obviously it is never necessary to go that far, for populations in a study area of manageable size will not ordinarily exceed more than a few hundred individuals of a given species. Therefore after the first eighteen animals, when one begins to clip two toes, it is possible to restrict surgery to that small complement.

The marmosas present a problem because they possess thumbs on both fore and hind feet. I felt that these must be critically valuable to them in climbing, and consequently I restricted marking practices to their fingers. There weren't so many marmosas anyhow, and I never got beyond the one-clip stage with either species.

After these manipulations I tied the animals back in their sacks and hung them outside in the shade while they recovered from anesthesia. Again, they varied greatly in the time it took to regain consciousness. Eventually I would see one bag after another begin to pulsate with activity. The label directed me where to take each one. Sometimes a Zygo would shoot out of the opened sack and dart into the brush. If I had mistaken the degree of its recuperation, an animal might on other occasions take only a few wobbly steps and lie down. In that case there was nothing to do but move it to a shady spot and cover it lightly with a few large dead leaves—another fifteen minutes would give it time to get its feet on the ground. *Heteromys* seemed much more certain of where they were than the others. They might sit up tamely at first, turning their heads and sniffing, but then they took off as if completely oriented, either making a beeline for some distance in great leaps or else diving down a burrow that they knew only a few feet away from the trap. Marmosas had only one thought: to climb. And *Oryzomys*—

but I'll tell about my lack of knowledge of these charming rats later.

Meanwhile one may wonder why TRVL was interested in small mammals to the extent that they were so maltreated. I can confuse that question by repeating that a mammalogist, with no concern about viruses at all, would have followed most of the procedures already outlined. This is how you learn about rats. Five different arboviruses, whether "important" or not, had been associated with Bush Bush rodents, and it was mandatory to find how these animals lived and when they might make contact with mosquitoes. If the lab wanted information on small mammals in Bush Bush, I would try to dig it out.

Or would I? Good intentions are splendid, provided little beasts cooperate. At the precise time that we set up We House and I came to occupy what I felt was an adequate field station, populations of rodents and murine opossums began to slide into a progressive decline that continued during my remaining years in Trinidad. By the time I left, there were many nights when my traps—and Moon's —caught nothing. We never determined any cause for the phenomenon. It's easy enough to observe hordes of lemmings drowning themselves at sea in boreal latitudes, or to follow "die-offs" of superabundant species in temperate regions when carcasses attest not to suicide but more likely to epizootic disease. But in Bush Bush the disappearance was silent and invisible. Trapping success simply became less successful, though captured specimens showed no signs of illness or any other abnormality.

Expectedly, "rodent-associated arboviruses" declined at the same time. I failed to weep, for the circumstance afforded me the excuse I needed to devote more time to birds. Yet I did feel regret, because I had become attached to my trap line and to quite a number of familiar rodents and murine opossums that had established themselves as regular repeaters. The line began at We House, where the first four traps were located. From there I had slashed intersecting trails with a cutlass all over the northern tip of the island and had dotted traps wherever the cover looked inviting to my eye. Apparently my ways of thinking were not too different from a rat's, for just before the population crash I often caught twenty-one animals overnight at thirty-two stations. That is a good score on any trap line anywhere, and actually a fantastic one in a tropical jungle where ten per cent success is often adjudged good.

Of course by that time I was getting numerous "repeaters." A curious situation had developed, though further opportunities might have let me interpret it. Fully half the marked animals never appeared in the traps again. At first I put this down to wariness, but perhaps they had been victims of the die-off. Many of the others, however, repeated more often than expected. If one can imagine that some rodents and murine opossums regarded anesthesia and toe clipping as a horrendous experience, never to be risked again by entering a trap, others of their community remembered only that delicious spread of peanut butter and oatmeal. Amputated fingers be damned! They had now healed. Furthermore, the price of a meal now entailed no additional injections or surgery. I would turn a grasped animal out of its sack, make a toe count, an liberate it with no more than a "How d'you do?" Even chronically repeating Zygos learned not to struggle—or maybe I am crediting these animals with a longer memory span than they really possess.

Thus I began to learn the whereabouts of at least a few specimens. None wandered far. Trapping stations were set from 50 to 150 feet apart. A given rat might be taken in two adjacent traps but less often in three. Sometimes I would read a toe formula indicating that an animal had crossed from one side of the peninsula to the other. Careful rereading of the toes usually proved me wrong: I had counted correctly but entered "right front foot" instead of "left" on my note pad. Other checks served further to prevent mistakes: animals could neither shrink nor change their sex. Only a score of marmosas having been marked, I was less liable to error in documenting their whereabouts: they ranged more widely than rodents but still adhered to restricted domains.

Such information, although scanty, was useful to TRVL. Marmosas did not enter significantly into virus cycles, so far as we knew, but forest rats and mice appeared at times to be primary hosts. And the viruses were not all innocuous ones. Venezuelan equine encephalitis virus (VEE in our lingo), for example, can cause important epidemics in man as well as in horses and donkeys. When we found more than half the Bush Bush population of rodents with VEE antibodies, we could not doubt that they were important in perpetuating this virus locally. In that case, how far could they transport it? If they never crossed the swamp to the mainland, one need not consider them a direct threat to Trinidad at large, even though our small selves might be in jeopardy and wind-blown mosquitoes must remain suspect at greater distances.

Oddly enough, the mainland rodents disclosed a much lower rate of VEE and other virus infections than those on Bush Bush Island at that time. Perhaps not too odd, for these cycles involve special mosquitoes, and the flying fauna of Bush Bush Island had a number of signal attributes that occupied Tommy's working days and sleepless nights. Apparently Bush Bush simply afforded a special combination of habitats that favored VEE and other rodent-associated viruses because it supported not only appropriate mammalian hosts and arthropod vectors but also all the other ecological attributes still awaiting definition—plant life, aquatic and terrestrial; temperature, humidity, sunlight; who knows what else?

Until the population crash, that is. Thereafter I vainly set traps week after week, and Dries and Leslie wrung their hands as hordes of baby mice, inoculated with mosquito suspensions, thrived.

A notable aspect of this situation was that the few animals I continued to catch were almost all elderly. Whatever carried off the population must have struck at infants and young adults. I ended up with a few Zygos and *Heteromys* (*Oryzomys* had disappeared entirely) almost a year old—and that is quite a longevity record for an unprotected wild rodent, exposed every day of its life to attack from snakes, lizards, predatory birds and less abundant enemies. This made things even more dreary for viruses, because assuming that a mosquito miraculously obtained an infection, it could now bite only these old animals that were undoubtedly already immune. So far as viruses were concerned, such bites would be wasted since they could not "take" any more than a smallpox vaccination in a person recently successfully scratched.

I did everything I could think of to step up the trapping score. Had I possibly scared the animals away? Faithful repeaters denied that possibility. Perhaps the bait had palled. Someone told me that cotton, soaked in vanilla, was better than peanut butter and did not attract ants. I tried that, but matters remained the same. Moreover, Moon's results in the "removal area" paralleled mine. Therefore I could not believe that "trapping out" was the answer; if so, Moon should be suffering but not I.

Howlers continued to howl at dawn in Bush Bush Forest, but in some tropical way of their own my lemmings had swum out to sea.

Chapter 7

BIRD NETTING

*A*ll this time I had been not only admiring birds but working with them socially. The study of small rodents can be a recluse's avocation, but birds command team enterprise. Not that all my colleagues liked birds—I'm sure that Leslie and Dries abhorred them. Elisha Tikasingh found them interesting enough, but *he* abhorred getting up before the birds did. Wil Downs was a read bird buff, and Tommy came close to that state, though his allegiance remained strongly with mosquitoes and bromeliads. Yet our bird program necessitated a concerted arising long before dawn, because we had to get to our stations by daybreak, when birds are notoriously most active, and one man can't do the whole job in a flash that may last for only an hour or two. . . .

I must explain about Japanese mist nets, among other things. When I began to band birds in 1928, everyone used baited wire-mesh traps that operated either something like Hav-a-harts, with moving triggered doors, or else on a maze principle, so that entering birds found it difficult to get out. We trapped mostly on the ground, though tree-trunk traps for woodpeckers and nuthatches had been developed, and a special chimney contraption for swifts had been devised also. During summers we visited colonies of breeding sea birds and banded nestlings by the thousands, merely by picking them up. Mist nets were totally unknown to us.

Japanese peasants had for centuries woven nets out of their women's hair in order to catch birds of all sizes either for their own meager cooking pots or for sale in local markets. These nets were contrived in various sizes of mesh, depending on whether sparrows or sandpipers were available. Spread out, a net much resembled the ones seen above badminton courts except that they were assembled as several such nets in parallel. The patient industry that went into knotting individual long hairs from a maiden's scalp to weave a single panel of one net depresses me. Yet I believe the same labor continues today. The Japanese have caught on to the concept of nylon, which now spares coiffures of wives and daughters, but nets are still made by hand, so far as I know. Anyway, bird banders continue to get their nets from Japan, and cheap labor there must be the main reason why we don't manufacture them here.

Another explanation has to do with our game laws. Small birds are generally protected, and every bird bander must have a special permit to use Japanese mist nets. No one else can use them at all, so the market in our country is really too small to encourage national enterprise.

Why *mist* net? I suppose the word refers to the near invisibility of the forty-by-eight foot snares, because the strands are so fine. Since they are (usually) black, they reflect no light. One can scarcely see them when they are set against any ordinary background such as a row of bushes or a forest's edge, which is where they are most effective, for birds are forever darting in and out of such marginal habitats between open areas and more sheltered ones.

The net is set somewhat loosely, so that an unsuspecting bird flying into it becomes lodged in a pocket of strands. Meshes of nets designed to catch small birds are about an inch square— big enough to permit a head to protrude through one, a wing through another, and feet and legs elsewhere. Thus the creature can't get a purchase on anything solid to aid its escape. Of course it struggles. The longer it is held by the net, the more entangled it becomes. An ornithologist saves both the bird and himself much grief if he keeps an alert eye on his nets and removes the captives as quickly as he can.

The first thing to determine is the direction from which a bird entered the net (if it was not actually seen flying to its engagement). This is not nearly as simple as it may sound. All of us wasted enormous amounts of time—were it all added up—trying to remove birds from the wrong side. Once you locate the pocket, extrication becomes fairly routine. Since toes are the most active grasping organs, it is wise to free them first. Now the bird can be held by its feet, which reduces its struggling to a large extent. Then the meshes may be dislodged one by one from the body and wings, until finally only the head remains to be disentangled— usually a simple act unless the rear of the barbed tongue has engaged one of the nylon strands. Then a most delicate touch is required.

When we arrived at one of our netting areas, usually just as light began to appear in the east, our first task was to get the nets into position. Depending on the territory, we used from six to a dozen nets. At the time each area had been selected, we had driven short lengths of pipe into the ground as permanent sockets for bamboo poles on which the nets were to be strung. Thus we had only to distribute the poles (which had been wired on top of the station wagon). We knew approximately where the pipes were situated, but often they were concealed by newly grown grass or fallen leaves. Time was now vital; I suppose a passer-by would have thought it ludicrous that a covey of scientists should be seen crawling about, probing the ground in semidarkness.

The poles being finally correctly lodged, nets were quickly stretched between them. It is possible for one man to set up a net by himself, but the task is much easier if two men cooperate. Each end of a net has five loops that must be strung and properly spaced on a pole. Until both ends are fixed, the center of the net has a tendency to sweep the ground, where its grasping meshes pick up as much litter as they can, and two men are better able to keep it taut during this maneuver. All the twigs and other debris must be removed, not just to give the net its full operating efficiency but again to render it invisible. Even if birds can't see the concatenation of meshes, a leaf ostensibly suspended in mid-air with no support must be so strange an object as to be frightening.

Now it was time to wait, though ideally some birds had already snared themselves before the last nets were spread. As in the case of fisherman's luck, some days were "good," others not. Our usual target was thirty-six birds, since that was about the maximum we could handle both in the field and at the lab. Each bird was placed in a cloth sack to await its turn for processing. Meanwhile the station wagon had been converted into a mobile laboratory. Syringes, needles, tubes, record books and bird bands stood in ready array. Bleeders went to work and then passed specimens to the banding department. Soon the birds were again on the wing—sometimes to fly right back into nets, for that's the way they were going in the first place! This time they were simply given a good toss into the air to help them along to their destinations. We didn't want to see them again that day.

These forays were weekly affairs that had been going on, though somewhat less elaborately or methodically, for years before my arrival in Trinidad. I think I was the only one who really enjoyed getting up at 3 A.M., but to me everything about it was delightful— not only the early dressing and breakfast, and later physical contact with birds with an opportunity to examine them intimately, but the entire general atmosphere of awakening and awakened dawn. To me this is the perfect time of day, whether one can see the sun rise or merely understand the struggle of light rays trying to penetrate from outer space a cloud canopy that is loath to let them through.

It was only natural, therefore, that I should quickly become a fixture on the bird-netting team and eventually its leader. Along the way we had many changes of other personnel. At first only the doctoral staff participated, Tommy being the most constant member. Dries and Leslie each came out just once "to see what it was like," rapidly satisfying their curiosity. Later we broke in various lab technicians as trappers and bleeders: the poor chaps had no choice but to follow orders and had none of our incentives to compensate them for disrupted nights.

Then, too, we sometimes put our longer-staying guest investigators to work. Leslie's argument was that "it was good for them." If they came to learn about TRVL, he reasoned that they should not omit any part of our doings from their experience—after all, he himself hadn't. And that brings me to Tak, who was by far the most imposed upon of these friends.

Dr. Mitsuo Takahashi came to us from the National Institute of Health in Tokyo, where he is an entomologist for the Japanese B Encephalitis Unit. His real purpose was to enlarge his knowledge of mosquitoes, but he acquired substantial doses of other lore during the ten months he was with us. It so happens that one of the very common birds in Trinidad, the Silver-beak Tanager, can "bite" like fury, and it seemed always to be Tak's lot to be the one closest at hand when a silver-beak entangled itself in a net. Even if the site was not in view, we could hear Tak's wails as the bird nipped one tender oriental finger after another.

Eventually Tak began to dream about his ordeals. One morning as we were driving through the dark, he regaled us with the following recital: "I had very good dream last night—about bird netting. I dream we catch Japanese crow, pheasant, wild ducks, wild pig and two tomatoes. . . . And Tommy catch a Silver-beak and it bite him. And Tommy cried and said, 'I am an entomologist!'"

Jap B virus, which can seriously affect human beings, is considered a "bird-associated" virus, as VEE virus is associated with forest rodents. Thus Tak should learn to net birds and to remove them painlessly, as well as the subsequent bleeding and banding techniques. In Trinidad our ornithological efforts were similarly oriented to the study of certain "bird" viruses, so that Tak's experience here could be of direct use to him when he returned to Japan.

Our chief concern was with eastern equine encephalitis (EEE) virus, though St. Louis encephalitis was also important. For many years the tests on avian sera at TRVL indicated that a low percentage of birds was being infected with EEE virus every year. No illnesses or deaths in human beings or horses had ever been recorded in Trinidad, but knowledge that the virus was constantly active on the island gave us all an uneasy feeling—especially Leslie, who felt that the lab should be in a position of knowing when and where people might be at risk. However, nothing much was done (we didn't know what else to do) other than further collecting of specimens in scattered localities with continuing confirmation that EEE virus was a close neighbor.

Suddenly the situation became more threatening. In quick succession outbreaks occurred in British Guiana and Jamaica. Surely the same thing could happen in Trinidad, right between them. The British Guiana episode might have been caused by VEE virus, of course, but TRVL promptly isolated EEE virus from the brain of a race horse that had died in Georgetown. Retrospective inquiries disclosed that peasants' horses, mules and donkeys had been dying for some weeks, but nobody became excited until racing stables were affected. Fortunately no people died in British Guiana, but the Jamaican epidemic accounted not only for about seventy equine fatalities but also those of seven or eight human beings.

Our organization being a "regional" one, we were prepared not only to receive materials for diagnostic purposes from neighboring territories but to send investigative teams to study outbreaks on the spot. These are expensive ventures. No one begrudges them, however, for they liven up routine not only for the voyagers but also at the lab, where a flow of new materials may hold all sorts of unexpected viruses.

Tommy, Elisha and two entomological technicians flew to British Guiana. Working with a local veterinarian, they soon learned that most of the known equine deaths had occurred in the northeast, along the Courantyne coast, where there had recently been a serious plague of mosquitoes. Accordingly Tommy made arrangements to stay at a government "Travelling Officers' House" where meals were served and a veranda could be converted into a temporary field laboratory. He and his assistants collected and sorted mosquitoes, storing them in steel thermos flasks containing dry ice. A shuttle service was arranged with the owner of a small plane, so that frozen specimens could be shipped to Georgetown and transferred to a commercial carrier bound for Trinidad. In the reverse direction came empty flasks and fresh blocks of dry ice.

Elisha and the veterinarian meanwhile went about the countryside bleeding equines, obtaining histories of all the animals. Had they been sick? Had they had any sort of inoculations—against VEE, perhaps? Had they ever been anywhere else? Local physicians also helped in obtaining blood specimens from a sample of the human population.

These sorties are exhilarating, for during the week or two that they endure one talks, eats and sleeps in the atmosphere of the thing. The evening I arrived at the government house, I found everyone sitting about discussing not cricket or women but EEE. At once I was offered some "Russian beer," which had a mighty friendly taste of something stronger. It was. A popular brand of rum in British Guiana is called Russian Bear, but the Guianese pronounce "bear" as "beer."

I had come, naturally, to work on birds. Tommy's sojourn was already sufficiently long to prove that the mosquito plague had abated. The dry season had in fact commenced. I reasoned that birds inhabiting regions where water had formerly stood would be the ones most likely to have been infected and now to contain EEE antibodies. The low-lying Courantyne coastal strip is devoted chiefly to cultivation of sugar cane and rice. By this time most of the rice had been harvested, but there were a few remaining inundated green fields. To these, swarms of Yellow-headed Marsh Blackbirds flocked every day, to feed on the still milky rice kernels. Obviously this would be the best place for nets. During the next week I bled more than four hundred birds, most of them blackbirds.

Epidemics are tantalizing affairs because so often they are not recognized until they are practically over. Time and again investigators arrive on the scene after the fire is out. Tommy failed to collect virus-containing mosquitoes: all were tested at TRVL and all were blank. Although a few of my birds had antibodies, these were not (with one exception) blackbirds, so I had guessed wrongly about the provenance of EEE virus.

If an expedition yields principally negative results, one might well call it costly. On the other hand the experience itself must have value, if only in affording guides for the next occasion. Thus it is often useful to publish papers in scientific journals on "What I Failed to Do," or "What Didn't Happen," though most editors are acutely allergic to that kind of contribution.

We could do no less than send Tommy and his crew to Jamaica several weeks later. Once more the fire was already out when he got there, though his mosquitoes did yield a different, less important, virus previously unknown to exist on that island. My services were not needed, because the University of the West Indies had its own local team of bird collectors and bleeders. However, some time later I did invade that sister island as an advisor in setting up the kind of bird program that Leslie now insisted we must have in Trinidad.

Trap, mark, release and retrap, with bleedings along the way: if that is valid for the study of viruses in rodents, it should be equally applicable to birds. At a staff conference Leslie put it in my lap. What kind of bird program would give us the most fruitful and current information about EEE virus activity? Even if we could not predict outbreaks in man or domestic animals, TRVL must be in a position to say that we had "followed the situation" by all reasonable means; no one could come in from outside and show us something that had been under our noses.

I had two immediate answers, each hinging on the other. Bird-banding would give us the ability to recognize individual retrapped birds, just as toe clipping identified rats. And established netting areas, rather than random collecting all over the island, would give us the best opportunity to retrap banded specimens. Although we would lose something by restricting ourselves to a few small areas, that could not be helped. Our time and personnel could be extended only so far. If we made a poor selection of sites, that might be partly our fault, but at least we would have tried to exercise scientific discretion in choosing them.

My long association with the U.S. Fish and Wildlife Service at once provided a real prop to the speedily launched program. As Volunteer Cooperator No. 03802 since 1928, I was issued the necessary bands and carte blanche for their use, even if most of the birds were tropical and would never set wing in the United States. As Dr. Duvall wrote from banding headquarters in Laurel, Maryland, he was interested in EEE studies anywhere in the Americas. EEE is important enough along our Atlantic seaboard, and what with birds migrating between North and South America, who knows what connection there may be between a sick child or horse in Venezuela and another in Florida?

Our general serological survey had indicated a concentration of antibody-containing birds in the northeastern and north-central segments of Trinidad, excluding the Northern Range. Hence we went on several scouting expeditions and finally selected netting sites with the ill-assorted and unlikely names of Fort Read, Vega de Oropouche and Brazil Village. Now the question arose: how can we expedite a realistic surveillance program in three places on only one weekly Friday morning? At last we wrangled an answer, though many others might have been as good or better: we would work one month in each area in succession. That meant an interval of two months between four-week visits at any one place, and during that time many banded birds might have died, been killed or left the area. However, the only alternative would have been to choose a single netting site and work it mercilessly throughout the year. One egg in one basket!

Events justified our choice nicely. After several trimonthly rounds, our weekly list of repeating birds reached magnificent proportions. And after many additional rounds, we began renetting and rebleeding some specimens for the third and fourth times.

But once more we began and continued to work under a certain cloud of ignorance, for we did not know how long an infected bird's antibodies persist in its blood stream. Assuming that they endure for the life of a bird, and that the bird can live for five or six years, a single "positive" serum specimen still gave little information other than the fact that EEE virus had been needled into it by a mosquito at some time or other—something of which we were completely aware already. The urgent question was: when? If we could now bleed birds at three-month intervals, and read tests at the lab that said "negative, negative, *positive*," it would be possible to look up dates of capture and pronounce: "This Silver-beak Tanager, adult female, from Vega de Oropouche, experienced an EEE infection between July and October, 1964."

That's getting down pretty close to the truth of epidemiology.

Chapter 8

LISTS AND LIST MAKERS

Scientific records, such as those that permanently inform us of bird-band numbers and tests on blood specimens, stand at one extreme of man's endless tabulations. At the other is the "list." List making can become as severe a disease as stamp collecting, or even worse. In its incipient stages the malady is not to be recognized as the curse it will eventually be, and indeed many persons fail to develop addiction, drinking only the occasional innocent cocktail. For a list—any kind of list—may be actually therapeutic at first. As soon as man learned to count beyond ten, he undoubtedly began making lists for convenience's sake: mammoths or wild horses might exceed the number of his fingers and thumbs, and after that it was difficult for him to keep the figures in mind.

I, of course, am an inveterate list maker, otherwise I would not talk so bitterly about it. To my joy, I found a fellow drinker in Tommy, and together we indulged in many a list of the advanced variety, that is, the kind no longer serving a purpose or having any intrinsic value but kept up to satisfy only the distorted ends of competition and personal greed.

Tommy's form of the disease was a particularly painful one from which, fortunately, I suffer less acutely. That is the bizarre conviction that lists must, above all, be correct. I'll grant the basic logic of such a point of view, just as I would insist that whiskey must contain alcohol, but on the other hand I don't much care whether it is 90 or 100 proof—you can handle that aspect of things by modifying your intake. But not Tommy. Ever since he came to Trinidad, he had kept records of the numbers of every kind of mosquito that had been collected and inoculated into mice. Since over a decade had now elapsed, his figures had passed the one-million mark, but still they had to be precise down to the last mosquito.

What's so bad about that? The trouble is that you have to add these data in at least two different ways—first the total of all mosquitoes in individual years and then the total of individual kinds of mosquito for the whole period. When the two tabulations are summarized, the answers should come out the same. And woe if they don't! Let there be a discrepancy of only two or three mosquitoes and I'd say the hell with it. Somehow I'd patch up the table by falsifying an item here or there. When a million mosquitoes are involved, such dishonesty could make no possible dent in the scientific truth regarding mosquito-virus relationships.

But if you are as sick as Tommy is, those two or three mosquitoes loom as large as pterodactyls, totally obscuring reason and science with their horrible wings. Everything must stop until he can locate the missing few. Secretaries are taken away from important work and assigned as a team to the Record Room. Every ancient file is dusted off, stacks of cards are sorted, old field sheets are retabulated and adding machines spew ribbons of paper yards and yards long. Meanwhile other affairs of the lab come to a halt, for we are a team, as I have already emphasized. How can we proceed when the entomologist is off on one of his binges?

One fateful day in 1923 I bought a small pocket notebook, measuring about three inches by five inches, and wrote therein my first daily bird list. I've still got this treasure (as well as its more than forty successors). Even early misspellings—downey woodpecker, chimny swift—don't detract from the classic, for I *know* I saw those birds on the indicated day, which is after all what counts. My little notebooks actually contain the story of my life. If anyone were to ask me what I was doing in, say, October, 1944, I would turn at once to the appropriate book. There I would find an entry: "October 14, Barro Colorado Island. Barred Antshrike, Blue Tanager, Smooth-billed Ani," etc. "Oh, yes," I'd answer, "I was in the Army, assigned temporarily to Gorgas Memorial Hospital in Panama."

So far so good. No alarming symptoms there—at least not very alarming. Deterioration begins insidiously when bird watchers begin comparing lists. Until now the first sight of a previously unseen species has been a thing of utter joy: now it becomes the occasion on which one either catches up with a competitor or, more happily, gets a step ahead of him. No longer is there time to relish resightings of familiar birds. What was a rarity yesterday has now been ticked off on the list and must be dismissed, lest it occupy time in which the next novelty might have been seen. The most shocking example of this practice I can remember was the time Wil Downs and I located Lilac-breasted Rollers in Kruger National Park, South Africa. These are as remarkably beautiful birds as their name suggests and merit eternal reverent looking-upon. On the afternoon when we spotted the first one, we observed it in ecstasy, reveling in our great fortune. Next day, as we searched for other thrills, a bird darted past and perched nearby. Up went our binoculars, and in unison we huffed, "Only another damned Lilac-breasted Roller!"

This is "life-lister's disease," and few ornithologists are immune to it. Almost every bird watcher, from the professional to the veriest amateur, can tell you how many kinds of bird have been recorded in his county or state and how many of them he has seen. Ambitious and sophisticated neophytes project their accomplishments against the formidable total recorded in the American Ornithologists' Union's *Check List of North American Birds.* As in other degenerative ailments, advanced stages become more difficult and hideously expensive to deal with. County and state having been exhausted of likely new life listers, the ravaged victim must now close his conscience, dig into his pocket, and plan his vacations to increasingly distant mountains, shores and plains.

By the time you are as incurably doomed as I am, the enterprise has become a meaningless travesty. My "world" life list of 1,561 species (as of November 4, 1965) brings sighs of envy from many a young novitiate who has just had his first puff of marijuana. The figure 1,561 looks mighty good to me, too—I love it and am proud of it. But does it mean that I could recognize all these birds if I were to see them again? Not for a minute! When I go through my notebooks, or the card file I compiled from them, I can accurately visualize no more than a third of them, perhaps fewer than that. The rest are only names, although I know what each one should mean. In a way the magic number has less to do with birds than with myself. It is as if a gourmet had kept a tally and could say, "I have had 1,561 excellent meals in my life," without being able to remember much of what he had eaten while vividly recalling gustatory and gastric satisfaction. The life list, then, is first a status symbol among bird watchers but finally a personal reminder that one has lived, even though death now be closer. One thing it is not, and that is ornithology.

My forgetfulness humiliated me but could not quench the thirst for more lists. If I could not encompass mental pictures of 1,561 species of birds, perhaps it would be possible to conceive of them in blocks. A splendid means for doing this came my way when Van Tyne and Berger's *Fundamentals of Ornithology* was published. Now I had in my hands a synopsis of birds of the world, divided into 27 orders containing 169 families. Surely the dullest mind would be able to recall whether or not its cells had ever been stimulated by a warbler or a thrush—any warbler or thrush would do.

Well, then, let's settle for the 169 families. How could one increase that sort of life list? Could one hope ever to complete it? To my relief, I discovered that there are no families confined to forbidden areas such as Red China, so that all were physically accessible. Moreover, a tremendous amount of stimulating travel would be necessary. Several families were restricted to the island of Madagascar, now Malagasy. Many others could be seen nowhere but in Australia or New Zealand, while one, containing only the aberrant

Kagu, would require a trip to New Caledonia, where chances of seeing the bird were dwindling because it is not only almost flightless but also almost extinct. I should have to hurry for that one.

Meanwhile here was Trinidad with two unlisted families not more than a few miles away, if I could but locate them. One was composed again of only a single species, the Swallow-tanager, nesting in the Northern Range but spending the rest of the year in South America. Wil Downs had seen it on several occasions, so that bird should offer no trouble. The other was a member of the South American family of screamers, in this case the Horned Screamer. Years ago these birds bred in Nariva Swamp, and Moon Jury told stories of having shot two recently, but no qualified ornithologists had seen them in ages. However, that remained as another possibility.

Across the water in Venezuela, within eyeshot from Trinidad on clear days, were many additional families that invited only a short expedition to see them—things such as trumpeters, finfoots, sunbitterns and puffbirds—while farther south, but at least not on the other side of the world, were a dozen other candidates. When we made our EEE excursion to British Guiana, I took an afternoon off and picked up the Hoatzin (called Stinking Jenny by the Guianese), a strange chicken-sized bird living in low trees and bushes along banks of rivers and creeks. Its unfledged babies are famous for diving from nests and swimming underwater to safety, later climbing back with the aid of clawed wings as well as toes when danger has passed. That brought my family list to 121, so I had only 48 to go. Even 121 is a wonderful list from a local point of view in the United States, far exceeding the number of available families in our own avifauna—the figure reflects my previous trips to Central and South America and former sojourns in India and Africa. In the United States I have seen all families but one: the Wild Turkey must feel itself slighted that I have not looked it up in my natal state of Pennsylvania.

This goal of completion is probably an impossible one to achieve. Orders of birds, yes; I think anyone could manage to glimpse one member of all twenty-seven of them without inordinate effort. But

some of the families are still little-known even to professional
ornithologists, having been collected infrequently and under difficult conditions. Plush-capped Finches of the Andean highlands, for
example, would be a formidable challenge for any vigorous and
bright-eyed young bird watcher, because the birds seem to be
scarce and in any case are prone to hide themselves. Seed-snipes
fall into the same illusive and irritating category. I doubt that I
shall make the effort where such efforts must be grim. How can
that attitude be reconciled with list addiction? I'll answer on the
post-Lilac-breasted-Roller basis: if I get a heart attack on an
Andean slope while trying to see a Plush-capped Finch, I would
cheat myself of seeing several other families from the cocktail
terrace of a hotel in Brisbane. And the longer I postpone Plush-
capped Finches, the less likely it will become that I shall ever see
them. Maybe, if I get a "second wind" at eighty, I'll make it. Or by
that time perhaps they'll have aerial sedan chairs from which one
can bird watch. At any rate, I know of no one who has seen all the
families of birds in his lifetime, and I intend to end up with a list
that is a near tie for the championship, if not at the very top.

One morning, as Tommy and I were driving to bird netting at
Vega de Oropouche, he said that he had made a list of birds seen in
his garden and tacked it on the kitchen wall in a place where he
could easily add new entries to it. "Why, so have I!" I replied, though
I kept my list on a closet shelf. Since we lived only one block apart,
this at once exposed the razor's edge of competition. Birds were
unlikely to favor one yard over another within that short distance;
we were immediately on our mettle as observers. We responded
with a definition of basic rules, to wit: we would count any bird
seen on the ground of the actual properties, on branches of trees
growing on the properties, but not where such branches extended
across property boundaries; including birds on branches of neighbors' trees when such *did* overhang the respective competitors'
properties; and also birds in such space overhead that extended as
far as the atmosphere's reach but still came within the compass of
a rectangular column of air that could be visualized as projecting

vertically to infinity from each property's legally defined boundaries.

Those were tough regulations and we played a merciless game. The vertical air shaft gave me a singularly helpful boost one afternoon, for Tommy was never able to match my record of a Man-o'-War Bird, known also as the Magnificent Frigatebird. This is a familiar marine species throughout tropical American waters. At many seaports as well as at sea it may be seen soaring on long, narrow, angled, motionless wings. The deeply forked tail completes an unmistakable silhouette. Occasionally frigatebirds cross Trinidad high in the air, at altitudes so great that they can undoubtedly see right across the island and therefore feel that they are in no sense "inland." While I was doing something unimportant in the garden that day, I happened to notice several frigatebirds engaged in the island-jumping maneuver. At first they were far to the west, but they seemed to be coming straight toward my tiny dot of earth. I ran inside for my binoculars and then watched their undeviating approach. It is difficult to judge a precisely vertical line over long distances: if a bird had passed over the neighbor's yard, it might still have appeared to me to be overhead. This is where binoculars helped me not to cheat, for the seven-power magnification should reduce errors in judgment by the same factor. Lying on my back on the lawn, I trained the binoculars straight up just before the frigatebirds arrived at the zenith, and in a moment one of them flew across the optical field.

Tommy was too full of admiration to display envy over that one. Anyhow, he remained far in the lead. For some reason—probably because he cultivated flowers while I specialized in vegetables— his garden attracted more kinds of hummingbird than mine. When I left Trinidad the score, as nearly as I can recall, was about 27–21, Tommy's favor.

Some amateur ornithologists are quite unashamed of their list addiction. They have a special name for themselves, "birders," to indicate that they are really serious about increasing their lists rather than frittering away time in appreciating birds aesthetically after the fashion of ordinary bird watchers or—worse—bird lovers. It is the birder especially who has taken to long-distance travel. We

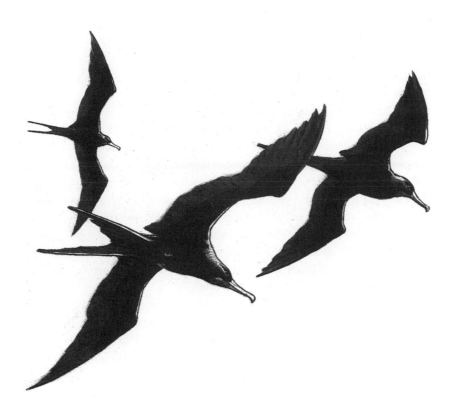

MAGNIFICENT FRIGATEBIRDS

saw quite a sufficient number of them in Trinidad. The word got around that I was a resident on the island, and before long I began receiving letters, asking whether I could meet this or that group and give them a conducted tour of the best birding places. Strangers to Trinidad, allowing themselves only a few days before zooming on to the next Caribbean resort, might easily search in relatively profitless areas. Besides, not knowing the birds, they would have difficulties in making identifications, whereas I could name at sight almost everything that flew. (That is another craven aspect of the birder. He would learn much more if he went through the protracted agonies of making his own avian diagnoses. But if we got merely a glimpse of a bird and I could say, "That was so-and-so," he cheerfully ticked it off on his list, still not knowing a blast about it. He *had* seen it, after all.)

I particularly remember one trio of birders who were about as ill as any that came to Trinidad. After a rather unsuccessful morning in the Northern Range, I took them southeast, past the Nariva Swamp and Mayaro, to a ravine heavily shaded by dense stands of tall bamboo. Suddenly the place was alive with a roving band of mixed tropical birds. Among them was a pair of Rufous-tailed Jacamars—long-beaked and long-tailed creations dressed almost entirely in iridescent green and bronze plumage. This represented not only a new species but also a new family for each of the birders. After they had exulted sufficiently, a lady in the party eyed me narrowly and said, "You're off the hook."

I try to persuade myself that she was only trying to be funny. Even if she were, she also meant it in part seriously, I'm sure. In other words, had the birds not cooperated—had I given up my day for these people and they had been dissatisfied—their displeasure would have been directed against me. Without knowing it, I had been on trial all the time. After that experience I was inclined to let visiting birders flounder by themselves.

But although the average birder may sell himself to the devil personally, he does no harm to his subjects. Indeed he is usually an ardent conservationist and is a strong force in his community and in the nation for promoting and upholding legislation that will protect birds. He is only rarely a hunter, and he even looks unhappily at so-called "justifiable" scientific collecting. My first real tropical birding took place in Honduras in 1930, when I had an opportunity to accompany an expedition from the Academy of Natural Sciences of Philadelphia, provided I would shoot and stuff birds. Thus at the early age of twenty-one I had to corrupt my better feelings. The motive was, of course, my bird list. But what good, I ask, was it to see a shadow in the bush, pull a trigger, and months later add a new name to my list after an unrecognized species had finally been identified at the museum?

Since then I have often attached myself to hunting parties, not to

RUFOUS-TAILED JACAMAR

carry a gun myself but to profit from all the chaos produced by others. In India we used to go duck shooting, or else it was a pre-Christmas foray for peafowl. Always I returned with life listers, though my companions thought this a poor return for a day's strenuous work in the field.

Probably one of my lowest acts was performed in Dutch Guiana (Surinam). Tommy and I had gone there to see about some arbovirus problems. I returned alone while he went farther to

French Guiana to study a mosquito which had suspected relatives in Petit Bush Bush Swamp. On my way back I found a small sparrow fluttering inside one of the windows of the airport near Paramaribo. Had I been able to recognize it, or had I been in civilized company, I would have liberated it gently outside. However, the bird was strange—obviously a life lister—and I was alone. Small sparrows are so much alike that I could not possibly have memorized all the tiny critical details that would lead to an identification when I got back to my books in Port-of-Spain. Quietly I exerted pressure on the thorax, in the way well known to bird collectors, almost instantaneously bringing an end to respiration. To justify myself, I inwardly observed that TRVL did not have this species in its collection. Of course that was not the real reason at all. And though the skin does repose in a museum tray at the lab, my life list now includes what it would not otherwise boast: the Grassland Sparrow, a South American representative of our Grasshopper Sparrow in the United States.

I think Tommy has avoided abysses such as this for several reasons. He has a very gentle nature, for one thing—or at least so it appears. The plucking of orchids and bromeliads from forest trees does not seem so much of a rape as the slaughter of a bird. Had he been an ornithologist, perhaps he would show up differently. He also makes many more lists than I, and this may prevent him from having to bury himself too evilly in any one vice. In Bush Bush alone he has found material for at least half a dozen lists—mammals, reptiles, amphibians, mosquitoes, ticks and various flies.

This demonstrates another hypothesis that I have considered as a possible origin of the list-making instinct. Counting fingers and toes is of incontestable practical value in the conduct of everyday life. But why should one multiply lists endlessly, or make lists of senseless things? (I used to make lists of the number of telephone poles along straight stretches of road between Bush Bush and Port-of-Spain.) It is the tendency to miserliness, which one sees developed in varying degrees in different people, from zero in the spendthrift to its full flower in our Fagins and Midases. Such zeal for overprotection has probably come down as an evolutionary heirloom from the days when hoarders survived a period of scarcity while their less acquisitive fellows starved. Squirrels that today store more acorns than they could possibly eat in a winter are undoubtedly behaving under influence of the same ingrained instinct.

There is one day in every year when I approach a list in innocent purity. That is New Year's Day, when I go out with a fresh notebook as clean as the new babe. In Trinidad I always went to the Caroni Marshes, just south of Port-of-Spain, to make the first entries. The reason I claim this as a pure action is that now I looked at every bird, to give each species a place on the new roster. Over and over I discovered forgotten pleasures in even the commonest finches and tanagers. I would make a New Year's resolution to forget about life listers and really take up ornithology. This mood lasted about as long as such resolutions usually do. By January tenth or fifteenth I would have recorded most of the ordinary birds and the old craving was back. . . . There is no help and no hope.

Chapter 9

THE GARDEN IN PORT-OF-SPAIN

A side from birds, Tommy and I had entirely different objectives in our respective gardens. I don't mean just the preference for flowers or vegetables, but something more fundamental. Like Ram Persad, Tommy insisted on keeping his garden in control, so that what grew there did so not only at his bidding but with his gracious consent. Ram Persad would really have enjoyed working for such a man rather than for me, because I held that even weeds can evoke sympathy from an observer with requisite curiosity and liberal views on what a yard may be permitted to look like. Since weeds are usually so much easier to raise, why not let them preach their gospels? Of course I let Ram Persad have his way most of the time, and the yard did look trim under his care. But now and then we would clash, whereupon he would pretend his best not to understand and I would have to call on Leon to make my point.

A further difference in Tommy's and my feelings about gardens stemmed, I think, as a corollary from the concept of being boss. He could view his avocado tree, for instance, as a servant representing all avocado trees. If he thought about it at all, his opinions would not have extended below the generic level. Had the tree not borne fruit bountifully, it would be worthy of discharge and replacement by a more obeisant one. Not mine. I became friends with it, and there was nothing it could do or not do that would ever mar my allegiance to its trunk and branches.

Imagine having an avocado tree outside one's study window! As a Northerner in the United States, I had held it unlikely that I would ever live in such a relationship. But for two years I was privileged to know this tree. It became, indeed, not only my friend but a teacher.

When I first occupied the premises, in late summer, fruiting had recently passed for that year. The tree was decked in broad green leaves which I assumed were a permanent feature of its appearance. But with onset of the dry season in January, leaf fall commenced, until the branches were almost bare. Almost simultaneously, however, terminal buds began to erupt with blossoms. The florets were not handsome, but they kept opening in profusion for months— without setting fruit! The performance bewildered me. Bees, hummingbirds and warblerlike Bananaquits visited the clustered inflorescences faithfully, but it seemed that pollination failed to take place or else the tree was too lazy to nourish offspring.

Finally new leaves began to appear. As if this were an awaited signal, tiny avocados the size of peas sprang from the last blossoms. Now I enjoyed the spectacle of their slow growth as the tree reclothed itself in foliage. Frequent counts never added up to the same figure, but I judged the tally to be about sixty young fruits. I had no idea whether this score was good or bad for a tree of this size—it was higher than our one-story house—but the crop would surely be too large for Leon and me to consume.

The globes expanded very slowly. I was told that avocado season occurred in July. Therefore I had ample time to decide what to do when suddenly sixty avocados demanded to be eaten. For one thing, I would fill the back seat of my car and make the rounds of all my colleagues' homes, giving each one as many as he felt his family could use before they spoiled. Naturally I would eat them three times a day myself. But in addition I was going to try freezing some of them. If that worked, my menu could boast out-of-season delicacies for many a month.

All this went according to schedule, except that some of my colleagues did not like avocados, others had trees of their own, and I did not eat them for breakfast while they were fresh. When I thawed the frozen fruits later, I found them awful, nothing like avocados at all—they were mushy and entirely distasteful. My daughter Valerie had written that she had read of a recipe for avocado soup, prepared something like vichyssoise. I attempted to prepare something of the sort, and it was horrible, too, although Leon finally finished it.

Afterwards Tommy told me I needn't have been so anxious about harvesting the crop all at once. Given a tree laden with mature fruits, he said, one can still pick them one by one over a period of time. An avocado, after being plucked, ripens within a few days. But if it is left on its twig, it remains in an arrested condition, stony hard, for weeks.

This had been an entrancing experience. Meanwhile I felt that my understanding of the tree had advanced from the primitive state of being attracted to it only gastronomically. The soil underneath its branches was bare of grass. In the dry season the ground was hard as a rock, and when rain occurred water drained away as quickly as it fell. To me it looked as if the avocado must be having a slim time eating and drinking.

Once more I tangled with Ram Persad but at last persuaded him to dig a shallow circular trench about six feet out from the trunk. Henceforth I had him and Leon run the hose into the trench several times a week, while I periodically sprinkled pellets of an all-purpose phosphate-nitrogen commercial fertilizer into it. Not that I expected perceptible results: this was only the sort of loving-kindness that true friendship generates. But the second year! The avocado never did shed its leaves; fruits began to set with the earliest blossoms; and the total crop was well more than double the first one. Moreover the "pears" were now so staggered in age that I would not have the problem of a simultaneous harvest.We ate the first one while final babies were still being nurtured at pea size. Leon was so impressed by one gargantuan pear that he carried it to a local vegetable market to be weighed. I was in Jamaica at the time, but on my return he reported that it had come to three and a half pounds and that he and his current family had taken two days to consume it. Truly the avocado had been suffering from tropical malnutrition all the time, like millions of human beings around the Equator.

The avocado had parasites—not viral, malarial or other counterparts of our own attackers but, among others, caterpillars. Here my concern for a friend became less that it should have been, because while I like trees, I am also devoted to caterpillars. Tommy had already told me of a species of silk moth that habitually lays its eggs on avocado leaves, so I kept an alert eye on domestic events. He said that the caterpillars were reputed to have venomous spines and were locally called "shinneys." This is a Trinidadian corruption of the French word *chenille*, meaning "caterpillar" or "worm." It has nothing to do with boys' being stung as they "shinnied" up tree trunks, as I at first assumed.

Eventually I detected a cluster of cubical, sculptured caterpillar droppings—"frass," as entomologists call them—on bare ground under the tree. Following that lead upward, I located a fat shinney on a branch to which I could climb. There was no choice but to pluck the leaf bearing the caterpillar and take it to the lab for a joint experiment. "You try it first," I invited Tommy. "No, you first, my dear Alphonse," he responded politely. (We both wanted to pioneer.) The larva was about an inch and a half long, rather fat, whitish in color, with a coating of sparse long hairs overlying tufts of shorter spines. The hairs were apparently innocuous, but the spines were stiff, ready for business.

I had often encountered caterpillars of this sort. In Pennsylvania one of the commonest is that which ultimately yields the beautiful Io moth. If one brushes against one of these larvae, the ensuing sensation is reminiscent of having stumbled into nettles—a sharp stinging, followed soon by itching, swelling and inflammation lasting about twenty minutes before all is again well. The spiny oak slug gives you an equivalent experience. Hence I felt no hesitation about pricking myself deliberately with the spears of a shinney.

What Tommy's previous personal knowledge of such things may have been, he did not say, but at the end of the coffee break, after all of us had discussed the project (everyone else considering us damn fools), he inoculated the back of his hand as freely as I with the tiny sharp daggers. Nothing! No nettles, no irritation. Then, after a lag of a few minutes, we began to feel something quite different. A bit of local discomfort bothered us, but that was nothing to the tremendous aching that set in and extended up our arms to the shoulder. I have never felt anything like it, nor has Tommy. Weakling that I am, I went home and tried to assuage agony by consuming a bottle of rum. Tommy stuck to his working schedule but told me later that while he was dictating to a secretary in the afternoon he would have to get up and stamp his feet in order to avoid screaming. As scientists, we both kept notes on the course of our travail. Comparing accounts later, we found that each of us had recorded amelioration of acute pain about six o'clock in the evening. That had been a long seige, not one I am likely to invite again for the sake of an experiment.

We looked at the shinney's spines under a binocular dissecting microscope and could see that they were brittle and hollow. When we broke one with fine forceps, the stub exuded droplets of a pale, oily-looking fluid. I suspect that it did have an oily base, like "long-lasting" penicillin, for otherwise the effects should have worn off sooner. However, this entomological-toxicological conjecture remains unverified. But were the active principle water soluble, its rapid absorption would have put it in the class of snake venoms, and Tommy's and my curiosity might have ceased to embrace new topics.

Shinneys infested my avocado tree in considerable numbers. When the caterpillars had completed growth, they descended along numerous branches and converged to one or two places on the trunk, near ground level, to spin cocoons in a sort of company. Here they contrived the most engaging kind of camouflage individually, though the community of cocoons could not be missed by even a casual eye. I was baffled by the contradiction and still am. A single cocoon could easily be overlooked, for its outer, spreading, low-lying case was woven loosely, and apparently with threads of varying colors, so that the structure matched rugosities of the avocado's bark. If cocoons had been dispersed, I would have had to search for them. But caterpillars resorted to the same sites year after year, and cocoons of former seasons now hung, tattered, as flags of the present consortium.

Interiors of the cocoons were spun much more firmly. I was astonished, on taking apart the layers of several of them, to find that the innermost shell was shaped angularly, something like a Brazil nut, and that one end had moreover been left virtually unsealed, providing a flap which the future emerging moth could push aside without ado. Moth? Indeed, that is what the cocoons yielded, but they were a disgrace to the usually gaudy giant silk-moth tribe. I kept a few cocoons on my desk. The reward was a succession of plain brown creatures that anticlimaxed their venomous but handsome avocado-feeding predecessors.

This tree clearly overshadowed other growing things in the garden, literally as well as in my estimation. However, I continued to revere weeds and everything in between. If I had any negative prejudices at all, they were toward plants that really ought not to have been there. "Exotic" is an inspiring word: in Pennsylvania one would apply it to orchids as well as avocados. My Trinidadian landlady saw things in a reverse sense and had cultivated some rare chrysanthemums and gladioli that did extremely badly in her flower beds but must have been some of her choicest herbs. Ram Persad tended these with special love. Repeatedly they came into bud, promising a glorious show, only to shrivel before their acme or to raise their faces for only a day. The same was true of some straggling carnations. Floribunda roses might have done better but for leaf-cutting ants. Native flowers and shrubs being so attractive and well adapted, I could never understand the motive for bothering about troublesome *Ausländer* unless it be the prod of that villainous word, "exotic."

On the other hand, my landlady may have had one point on her side. As with the rest of her neighbors, and indeed everyone in Port-of-Spain, she had a couple of very fine poinsettia bushes in the yard. Some places had whole hedges of them. These came into full color early in December, when everyone would say, "Christmas is coming." But contrary to our notions of greenhouse poinsettias in the States, where we can see them wilting in their pots soon after Santa Claus has left, poinsettias in Trinidad last practically until Easter. The result is that after the first few weeks you don't see them.

I never saw much attempt at effective fertilization beyond the occasional purchase of small loads of manure, expensive because it was in short supply. All one talked about was rain. If Tommy had had a gauge in his garden, we would have been off on another contest, for it so happened that I did. Often after a heavy shower, I might report to him that my garden had received half an inch. He might just as well respond that his hadn't had a drop. Some showers were as sharply marked off as that, giving our block-apart premises really strikingly different day-to-day histories, though over an entire season the precipitation probably averaged much the same.

Affluent people did use chemical fertilizers, which were abundantly available and expensive, but these have a tendency to be washed away during heavy downpours, because surface runoff of water does not give them time to seep downward. I have always been a great believer in compost, so one of the first things I asked Ram Persad to do was to dig a pit in an inconspicuous corner of the garden behind an everbearing lime tree. Into this we would throw all lawn and hedge clippings, as well as vegetable garbage. (Leon thought it was a trash pit, but I corrected that misconception after I discovered tin cans, papers and bottles.) Ram Persad was appalled at the idea but could only comply. I marked out an area about four feet square and handed him a spade. "How deep?" he asked hopelessly. His reluctance often irritated me, so I merely said to keep on digging until I told him to stop. When he got down to three feet (several weeks later), I took pity, though it should have been deeper.

Before we had a chance to fill the pit with rotting vegetation, it caught a small stray dog. Wild dogs are a plague all over Port-of-Spain. They come out mostly at night, roaming singly or in packs and upsetting every dustbin in town. People mix their garbage and trash, so that a dog often must scatter cans and papers widely to get at some edible morsel at the bottom of the container. In the mornings, streets and sidewalks are indescribably littered.

I don't know if the same thing happens elsewhere, but in Port-of-Spain most of the derelict bitches come into heat at the same time, about twice a year. Then for several weeks the nights resound with howls, yelps and snarls from all directions. Privately owned dogs, properly penned or chained within their own grounds, become infected by the ambient excitement and yowl even louder or more insistently in frustration. Most people keep at least one dog as protection against intruders, so the bedlam may be imagined.

Where "my" little dog came from I shall never know. While working in my study, I heard whines and thought that the neighbors might have bought a new puppy. The noise seemed too loud to be coming over the six-foot hollow-tile wall, and besides the neighbors were at home—pups wail mostly when they are left alone. I went outside and looked about, but the yard was now silent. Back at my desk, I soon heard whines again, louder now. This time I searched harder, at last discovering a brown and white dog cowering in the pit. Whatever her multiple ancestry contained, part of it was derived from a short-legged breed, for her pregnant belly almost dragged on the ground. She could no more have jumped than flown. As for climbing, the walls of the pit were vertical and offered no claw holds. I had been away for several days and now noticed that the earthen walls were scored all around with claw marks. Poor thing! she may have been there for a long time.

I was afraid to get into the pit to lift her out. Though canine rabies seems to be no hazard in Trinidad, I did not want to chance even a nonrabid bite. The best I could do was to lower a couple of boxes to create a stairway for her. Retiring to my study, I watched from the window. Just then a shower broke. Up came the small head, followed by a struggling body. The drenched animal paused a moment, staring balefully around as if to fix this inhospitable place in her mind, and then trotted off to—where? Perhaps she knew a dry shelter, or maybe the nearest dustbin was her destination, even in daylight.

Compost is tricky stuff anywhere—wonderful if you make it right, but otherwise serving more as mulch than fertilizer. I did not really care how mine turned out, for the important thing was to form some sort of cover for the vegetable garden, to hold rain some days and to prevent the earth from baking on others. Yet with the number of tropical pests one has to deal with, I sometimes found that materials in the pit had simply bred an army of enemies, such as snails, that quickly cut off young plants when I transferred a heavy layer to the bed. Cutworms, too, seemed to appreciate these efforts, and I learned eventually to wait until the present crop of okra or beans had matured enough to develop woody stems before surrounding them with shelters for predators. Leaf-cutting ants, though adversaries, were interesting from the standpoint of their selectivity. They adored okra but would not touch a bean or cucumber vine.

Following one particularly successful growing season, during which compost gave me mixed benefits, I read a gardening column in the daily paper which recommended excavation of vegetable beds to a depth of several feet and lining the bottom with bottles lying on their sides. These would become half filled with water during the rains, it said, and then slowly exhale moisture throughout the dry season. Roots would find their way deeply to the aquatic source. Perhaps one could then dispense with compost—or at least use it more sparingly.

Now I regretted having given Leon all my empty rum bottles, which he redeemed for two cents apiece. However, I could see the value of deep bulldozing and a liner of some kind of absorbent material. Once more Ram Persad received the gift of a shovel from me. This time he really did poorly, going down no more than two feet. But we managed to acquire a satisfactory mass of litter, including a dead palm tree that had to be cut down, and the bed came into its own after that.

With everything doing beautifully at last, I was puzzled by a malady of my Kentucky Wonder beans. These were trained to grow up poles and then to spread out laterally along wires between the poles. The plants were sturdy, blossomed and bore profusely, but their tops were always ragged and nibbled. I pried under every leaf, looking for snails or caterpillars; everything was clean. One day I saw the marauders in the act, and I have never been more enlightened: they were birds! Furthermore they were of a type that I would not have associated with a diet of blossoms and tender leaves. Tak used to dread Silver-beak Tanagers in the nets but he feared Grayish Saltators even more, for these large finches have beaks like metal shears. Yet here they were, flying over the hedge from a vacant lot beyond, snipping off the most succulent shoots in sight. I could not begrudge them their spoil, for it was beans that got this species on my yard list! I imagine this provender was baby food for nestlings.

Of course Leon's pigeons didn't count on the competitive list, since they are domestic. When he asked permission to keep some, I almost wept with approval, since I have been a fancier of these idiotic birds since childhood. His idea was to confine them to a small box, but that didn't please me at all. "We must make a real flying cage, to begin with," I said, "and after they have made a nest and laid eggs, we can put a door in it so they can go wherever they want and return at will. How nice they will look on the roof or walking about the lawn!"

Leon didn't take to that idea one bit. "Dey fly away, Doctor," he said.

"No, they won't," I insisted. "Just trust me—I know all about pigeons." I set to work and demolished a secondhand bookcase. With this lumber and a roll of chicken wire I fashioned a crude but effective cage outside the kitchen door, and soon we were in business. A nest was made, eggs were laid, the door was opened, and—the pigeons flew away. "Well," I said to Leon, "get some more birds at my expense, and this time we'll keep them in." Leon did, and one night a robber cut through the wire and stole them. We abandoned that project. But I still wonder what was wrong with the first pair; pigeons don't usually act that way, and I continue to contend that I understand them.

Often I would not get much farther than the kitchen door in my rambles—before my eyes were the pigeons, the avocado tree, the everbearing lime, the compost pit, the rain gauge and the vegetable garden. Yet it took only a right-angle turn and a few more steps to reach the orchids and the papaya tree. The orchids were of two species, both of the sort that has its own roots in the ground rather than clinging solely to branches. These did cling, but only for support. Their trellises were two calabash trees that had been planted for that express purpose—not to grow calabashes. Ram Persad regularly trimmed enterprising shoots so that the orchids could monopolize all the sun's rays.

One orchid was of a purple variety with an inflated lip, very commonly seen in gardens all over Port-of-Spain. I called it a vanilla orchid, though Tommy told me it was only a relative of that species. The other, a spider orchid, was less handsome but in a way more bizarre, bearing long sprays of a dozen or eighteen blossoms, each with narrow, twisted petals speckled with wine-colored dots. Both these "exotics" (to me) were interesting garden pets, but somehow I felt sorry for the calabash trees. Had they no rights?

And why calabash? I learned that this tree has a peculiarly spongy, corklike bark that makes it especially hospitable to holdfast aerial orchid "roots." These in no wise strangle the trunk; nor are the orchids parasitic. The calabash must simply endure as a living, cropped skeleton in order that some human being may admire orchids. Enough of that! I wanted the calabashes to have calabashes. On the way to Bush Bush I passed many peasant yards where the calabash was cultivated for its real function: the production of gourdlike fruits that could be used as water containers. But I had never seen how the trees blossomed or how the gourds developed.

The response was lovely. Obedient branches spread as if let out of school. I examined them for blooms as often as I got that far in my tours of the yard, and I was pleased to note that the orchids didn't seem to mind at all. But Leon gave me a jolt one day. "Perhaps de calabashes both males," he said. Until then I had not realized that calabashes are one of the "two-houses" plants, with sexes in separate quarters. In any event, neither tree blossomed while I resided in that yard, and I shall have to begin this whole project again in some other time and place.

But the sexual angle was totally familiar to me when it came to papayas—"pawpaws," as they are called in Trinidad and other former British colonial possessions. In the front yard, beyond orchids and calabashes by a few more steps, were two small flower beds that seemed waste space to both Leon and me. With my approval, but not Ram Persad's, Leon soon had them lush with tomatoes and sweet peppers. To accomplish that, he had diverted part of a load of manure meant for my beloved okras. And therein lay a seed.

You can't tell a papaya's sex when it is a baby—I can't, anyhow. If you have only one, the chances for harvesting eventual fruit may be poor even if it is a female, for these plants depend on birds and insects for their pollination, not wind. Therefore a small grove is the logical thing to have, a mixed company of males and females close together. Flying nectar feeders flit back and forth from one to the other, and the females are soon weighted down with circlets of globular fruits like many-breasted Hindu goddesses. The lone female papaya may well live to bloom and blush unseen.

Nevertheless I wanted to observe the growth of this solitary plant as another of my introductions to the personal problems of a tropical species. Ram Persad being sufficiently warned, the "tree," if it can be called that, now gave me a year of intense pleasure and anguish. It grew at enormous speed—about a foot a month—spreading its dissected leaves into a crown over a yard wide and pushing away the soil as its trunk expanded with amazing force. Yet the trunk seemed as soft and delicate as any succulent asparagus spear, and far more beautiful. At this stage of burgeoning growth, before it had become densely fibrous, the cuticle bore splotches of lavender against a light green background, duplicating the hues of a luna moth.

One really should put an end to expeditions when papayas crop up in vegetable beds. But Bush Bush kept calling, and I could study this one only in stages. Returning once, I discovered evidence that it was a female. Buds of future blossoms had set singly in recent leaf

axils, whereas a male would have formed them in clusters. That set
me off in my car on a canvass of the neighborhood, to see if I could
discover any potential husbands in the vicinity. Many nearby yards
were open to view, but others were enclosed by hedges and walls.
Thus although I did not see any males, I could not be certain that
adjacent mates were lacking.

Besides, I knew that much more serious jeopardy than spinster-
hood shadowed this tree. While I was coming to Trinidad, a fellow
passenger on shipboard informed me that papayas had in recent
years been stricken by a blight which (from its description) sounded
to me like a plant-virus disease. After having been one of the most
common and easily raised fruits on the island, they were now rarely
seen in the markets. This was a blow, for I had become a papaya
devotee in India. Oddly enough, citrus fruits in the deep tropics
are often of inferior quality, and a really good papaya, sprinkled
with a few drops of fresh lime juice, comes as a lifesaving breakfast
companion.

A few blossoms on my tree miraculously "set"—I gave thanks to
roving bananaquits for that, though perhaps I should have been
grateful also to the Common Emerald Hummingbirds that infrequently hovered at the flowers. Little fruits began to swell. Then I
came home from Bush Bush to find that blight had struck. It was an
insidious type of malady, for it did not kill the tree outright and
openly. Rather, it attacked the broadest green leaves, yellowing
them in a number of spots near their centers. The spots gradually
coalesced, until the tree would shed stricken members one by one.
All else, however, seemed to be in order. Fruits showed no trace of
yellow, the trunk continued to expand, and the terminal cluster of
young leaflets looked as flourishing as ever.

For a long time I pondered whether a tree could become immune
following a siege of virus infection, the way we are able to do. After
the diseased leaves were discarded, I could see that growth had
been retarded during the acute stage of illness, for leaf scars were
crowded together on the section of trunk that should have expanded
at that time. But now a second burst of foliation occurred. A new

crown exceeded the older one in extent, and leaf bases spaced themselves in accord with photosynthetic freedom.

Alas! This was not immunity but only a remission. I harvested six papayas from the first cycle and three from the second. A third relapse—or was it the fourth?—brought the tree to its end, with disease finally and mercifully destroying its vitals to the roots. Ram Persad cooperated delightedly in exhuming it and casting its remains into the compost pit. I had only admiration for its pluck—and a lasting knowledge of that lovely lavender and green skin when life was indifferent to future viruses.

Chapter 10

SOLDADO ROCK

*R*ewarding as back-yard excursions may be, one occasionally wants to break out into wilder activity. When no such escape is possible, people are reduced sometimes to the unfortunate state of a South African lady I read about in Johannesburg who went to bed for seven weeks with a clutch of ostrich eggs, hoping to hatch them. (She succeeded, although someone raped her in the course of her dedicated incubation.) Happily we had more stimulating opportunities for mental and muscular release in Trinidad, though Tommy and I did almost go to bed with some baby Sooty Terns, as I shall now relate.

Richard and Margaret ffrench led us to our adventures on Soldado Rock and a new virus for Trinidad. Richard is a tall, thin, lively Englishman who teaches in a boys' school maintained by one of the big oil companies for children of its employees in Point-à-Pierre, near San Fernando, in southwest Trinidad. Somehow he became interested in birds. Having done so, he made it his duty to do something constructive about it. Through a process of devoted self-education, he finally became proficient enough to be given a permit by the U.S. Fish and Wildlife Service to band certain birds. That agency, in turn, was eager to find volunteer cooperators in the tropics who would trap and band migrants from North America. The possibilities in Trinidad included ducks, gulls, terns, shore birds, Dickcissels and a few species of warbler. Richard ffrench was a natural for the F. and W. people, just as they provided the exact outlet he wanted for himself. He selected Dickcissels, shore-birds and terns as his specialties.

I believe that Tommy met Richard at a meeting of the Trinidad Naturalists' Society. Anyhow, tales of tern banding on Soldado Rock fired Tommy's strenuous knock-yourself-out instincts, and Wil Downs responded with equal muscle flexing when a joint venture was proposed. As for Richard, he welcomed not only the thought of bird-minded companions but also the extra pairs of hands. Sooty Terns and Brown Noddies on the Rock had to be caught first— whether as flying adults or scurrying chicks—but it was not simply a matter of banding and letting them go. Each bird must also be weighed; certain measurements must be taken; stage of molt or lack of molt had to be detailed; and at least one person must be on hand to record data in the proper notebook as items were called out.

Formerly Margaret ffrench had been No. 1 assistant in all these tasks. Occasionally Richard would persuade one or another of his slightly interested friends to help, but they did it more for adventure than out of understanding. Now TRVL became a real partner in the enterprise, for the first trip was so unexpectedly profitable that Soldado was added as a fixture to our program.

Soldado (Soldier) Rock lies about ten miles west of the southwestern tip of Trinidad, rising some hundred and forty feet above sea level from the shallows of the Gulf of Paria. To get there, we would drive from Port-of-Spain, pick up Richard and anyone else from Point-à-Pierre who was going, and then continue through oil-fields within the jungle to Cedros. Here the boatman was waiting with his small but heavily built wooden craft, equipped with a powerful outboard engine. Now we lugged load after load of needed equipage across the beach, sometimes standing in water above our knees to heave heavier articles on board.

Off we would chug, the motor as likely as not conking out from time to time. The Rock looked tiny at first—as it really is, covering only about two acres on the map. (Its actual surface is much greater than that because of its steep sides.) But as we neared it, after an hour, concepts of tininess went up the spout: now it was formidable and forbidding. All around its perimeter lay great fallen blocks of stone, against which waves crashed in foaming fury. As if to head us off, flocks of grotesque Brown Pelicans leapt into the air and set up a patrol round and round the rock near sea level.

The boatman knew a small, hazardous inlet on the far side. Here, while his craft bobbed against boulders with each incoming and out-flowing wave, we formed a bucket brigade, he handing things from the boat to a succession of people progressively less submerged until finally all items reposed safely above water line. The outboard then found its voice, and away went our contact with civilization. To-morrow, if all went well, the boat would return. But meanwhile we were as shipwrecked as the most celebrated castaways in literature.

Our first trip was not that dramatic, for we had come on only a day's outing. Disembarking was just as adventurous, however, as was also the climb up to the "saddle." The slope looked almost straight up, and it was composed of guano mixed with decomposed rock of some sort, the whole substrate slipping out from underfoot with each step. A few low bushes and plants appeared to offer hand-holds, but these pulled out when grasped. Besides, we quickly concluded that the vegetation should be spared, for it was the only cover available to shelter young birds and, surely, to prevent total erosion.

Nor were fledglings its only beneficiaries. On our approach to the Rock we observed large iguana lizards (not a marine species, as in the Galápagos) traversing cliff faces, and here on this scarcely less vertical though lightly vegetated ascent we found their nursery. Numerous babies—green creatures less than a foot long—invited collection, but already they were either fleet or else incredibly knowledgeable about crevices inaccessible to our acquisitive hands.

Soldado is topped by a small peak, but below that is a narrow ridge, fairly level—the saddle—where we camped on future occa-sions. Today it was the chief collecting ground for Richard's band-ing ambitions. Sooty Tern chicks ran about in various stages of development and could be caught by hand either as they cowered

SOLDADO ROCK AND SOOTY TERNS

against the ground, seeking to escape notice, or else if driven into rocky cul-de-sacs. Brown Noddies were still incubating eggs, so this excursion served to prompt plans for a date on which babies of that species would be equally vulnerable to capture.

Sooty Terns are handsome black and white birds with deeply forked tails. Noddies cannot be described as enthusiastically, though their pearly white caps are indubitably attractive. As we advanced up the slope and along the saddle, the air was filled with distracted adults of both species, Sooties clamoring constantly in the voice that has given them their mariners' nickname of "Wide-awake," Noddies living up to the less vociferous designation implied in their Latin designation, *Anoüs stolidus*.

Wil and I weren't much help to Richard at first. Having huffed our way to the ridge, we now had to see where we were. Eastward, the southwestern tip of Trinidad showed plainly on the horizon, while to the south one could see palm-fringed shores of the Orinoco Delta in Venezuela (though it required binoculars to make out the palms). The latter area looked completely uninhabited, despite the presence of primitive Amerindians. A bit to the northeast, we identified oil rigs in the Gulf of Paria. Thus the Rock commanded a panorama embracing extremes in the stages of civilization, while itself being so primordial as to antedate them all.

Next we had to get out our cameras, which wasn't much aid to Richard either. How helpful was Tommy being? He, I fear, was the least useful of the whole party. When we brought our eyes back to the local scene, we found him on his hands and knees, turning over small rocks one at a time and popping dotlike objects into glass vials.

"Ticks!" he exulted. "Hundreds of them!" Sure enough, almost every stone covered several tiny, leggy creatures that could be plucked with fine forceps and transferred to collecting bottles. And herein lay the success of our day. I don't know how many terns Richard banded, but those ticks gave us our first inkling of the presence of a bird virus on Soldado Rock.

The virus was an annoying one in many ways, but therefore the more challenging to scientific investigators. At the lab it behaved erratically, and after several passages in mice we lost it. Meanwhile other workers had found what appeared to be the same virus in similar ticks from Sooty Tern and Brown Noddy colonies in the Dry Tortugas Islands off Key West. To verify the identity of the two viruses, we would have to re-collect it on further tick-seeking expeditions. Also, it now was obvious that we must look into the possibility of a relationship between ticks and birds as cycling agents for the virus: was it solely a tick virus, or did it depend also on periodically nesting avian hosts for annual perpetuation? It was childishly simple to assume that birds were involved, but a demonstration would be necessary.

Tommy did not consign the ticks indiscriminately to the grinding mortar and pestle—some had to be saved as pets, which should be rephrased as "objects of study," in deference to Tommy's qualifications as an unsentimental scientist. He soon identified them as *Ornithodoros capensis,* a name that can indicate at least part of their remarkable interest even to a layman. The genus *Ornithodoros* includes many medically well-known ticks that transmit diseases such as relapsing fever and typhus to man. But *capensis* is derived from the Cape of Good Hope, where this particular species was first discovered. The tip of South Africa seems a long way from Soldado Rock. But tick collectors have found it even farther afield—indeed, *O. capensis* seems to exist on warm islands and seacoasts all around the world.

That sort of distribution bespeaks transport by birds. If such were the case, what kinds of bird could circle the Equator to spread ticks so far? Actually the dissemination might be accomplished in relays, over many millenia, so that one need not propose even a limited number of avian agents as the responsible ones. However, Sooty Terns fit the proposition very neatly. They are a so-called "tropicopolitan" species, with known breeding colonies in all the oceans between the Tropics of Cancer and Capricorn.

Nevertheless, some arguments could be raised against that hypothesis. Fairly extensive banding studies indicate that these terns come back to the same islands where they were born, rather than to foreign ones. Thus if ticks clung to them during their absence over the waves, they also would be deposited once more on home ground.

But in addition it appears that young Sooty Terns, which are most heavily tick infested, go to sea and remain there until they are ready to breed, which may not be for several years. Could ticks postpone their own reproduction that long? Tick eggs must be laid on the soil and would perish in ocean wastes.

Scarcely believable but probably true is the recent suggestion that fledged Sooty Terns, leaving their natal island, fly *constantly* for three to five or six years before setting foot again on anything that will support their weight. Attesting this mad idea are several convincing points. When terns finish breeding, they do not come back to the islands at night to roost; they are not seen again until they are prepared for the next nesting cycle. Sooty Terns are never seen offshore during the nonbreeding season. They have been observed only in mid-ocean, far beyond a day's flight from a resting place. The number of perches on floating jetsam in mid-ocean is far too small to provide roosts for millions of Sooty Terns. And—most convincingly—it has been demonstrated that Sooty Terns are not naturally buoyant. Unlike other gulls and terns, if they are forced to alight on water, their feathers become saturated and they sink. There is nothing for them to do but keep flying.

During several years as constant aeronauts, perhaps some Sooties do out-Magellan Magellan several times, but there is no evidence that they span much more than a quarter of the globe. The wide distribution of *Ornithodoros capensis* is more likely to be the result of rare mistakes, occasioned by such unusual forces as hurricanes, rather than regular flights of Sooties or other birds. Perhaps even driftwood has contributed by transporting derelicts for long distances. Ticks of this genus are famous for their ability to survive for long periods without a drop of blood. When I left Trinidad, some of Tommy's early pets were still doing fine in their sterile vials.

Noddies were not as suspect, for in their supposedly stolid way they do come to land to roost at night; on some of our visits to Soldado Rock, when neither species was breeding, we would nevertheless witness a silent influx of Noddies at dusk. Therefore it would be difficult for them to span great jumps of longitude between oceanic islands, unless at some seasons they set out on more than local journeys and then resigned themselves to continuous flight: once again, we have no evidence of such behavior in Noddies. The ways of most sea birds remain little known.

Obviously we had engaging subjects for endless study, but we could spare only odd week ends for the game. The first venture impelled us to return quickly, because baby Noddies would be ready a few weeks later. This time we were a somewhat different party that included Tommy, Elisha, Tak, the ffrenches and one of their energetic lady friends. Adventure always flanked these trips: now it happened to be a matter of Venezuelan fishermen who had kidnaped some Trinidadian fishermen a few days previously in one of their chronic wars about custody of waters in the Gulf of Paria. Although Soldado Rock belongs officially to Trinidad, some Venezuelans think that the whole of this small country has no right to be independent of them, and Soldado is certainly no more than an offshore jot, only a step or two from the continental mainland. The Trinidadians were thrown into a jail without sanitary facilities. Their captors proclaimed: "If anyone wants. them back, let the Prime Minister himself come to collect them."

Consequently we eyed the few boats we saw with some excitement, though we were not really apprehensive. The little Spanish we knew would have been enough to convince antagonistic *Venezolanos* that we were fishing only for birds, the ladies' presence further validating our case. One boat came quite close, but our captain, after first deviating his course to avoid it, recognized friendly Trinidadians in the hull.

So at last we came again to the point of disembarkation and to the task of lugging everything up the slope. Here I must confess myself a slacker. I carried an army knapsack, containing personal necessaries, over my shoulder, and I toted also a single light object —a camp cot—under one arm; but as well I had to propel myself up the goddam hill, and when I got to the top I was completely fagged. "Sorry," I announced, "but I can't go down for another load. If I did, I'd never make it again." Forthwith I spread out the cot and dug into the knapsack for one of my "necessaries," which naturally was a bottle of rum to go with the sandwiches. When my companions returned with further loads, I applauded them as I happily surveyed the matchless panorama once again, with no cares for tomorrow or even tonight.

For tonight was to be crucial. From a virus standpoint, Tommy wanted to catch and bleed a large number of adult Noddies, to determine whether they contained antibodies to the new virus. Richard, too, preferred to study adult birds, because these gave information about molting sequences that babies could not provide. In addition, a banded adult is a better risk for future recapture, since mortality among fledglings may be staggering.

Once again I failed to pull my weight, except that I passed the rum bottle. But when darkness arrived and everyone else donned head lamps to go creeping along the cliffs to capture dazzled birds, I remained comfortably on my cot, observing the evening sky. In a way I was as anxious as if I were on the prowl, too, for the structure of Soldado Rock has been weathered by centuries of wind, rain and salt spray until the exposed stones have a cheesy texture. They look solid, but suddenly a grasped prominence comes away in your hand or breaks apart where you have placed your foot. Go tern catching with a head lamp in the dark on such cliffs? Not me!

Yet that was the choice of my friends, and I shivered for them. Each bird they caught was tied into a cloth sack, where it would repose until tomorrow morning. The team chased Noddies for hours, and as people came worn out to their own cots, I was roused from half sleep into a delightful interim of contemplation. The night could not have been more perfect. Sleeping under the sky is an experience which too few people ever enjoy, and those who appreciate it indulge themselves too rarely. The heavens were magnificent, with many a constellation I could not name. But no smog or reflection from civilization sullied the stars' immaculate clarity. Each flame jettisoned itself on the eye, as if these were anticipating our own silly plans to pay them a visit.

I don't know what the usual behavior of Brown Pelicans may be, but whenever we camped on Soldado Rock they *never* went to bed. Round and round the island they continued all night long. Frigatebirds kept them a remote sort of company. A hundred or so of these

long-winged fliers persisted in getting between me and my view of
stars and planets. I assume that they were sleeping, for they all
congregated in the same piece of sky, exactly where the prevailing
easterly wind cascaded up Soldado's exposed cliff. But it was phe-
nomenal how motionless the birds could remain. I would single out
one frigatebird that was obscuring a particular star and count the
seconds until I could see the same star again. Sometimes half a
minute would elapse until that soaring wraith had deviated far
enough in somnambulism—is there a more appropriate term?—to
give me a further look.

In such solitude company is a comfortable sensation. The various
cots and sleeping bags were clustered close together on the small
suitable area of the saddle. For the previous two hours, whenever
I opened my eyes I had seen the winking of head lamps as my colleagues climbed perilous cliffs to catch birds. Now that they were
asleep, I noticed that we could claim weak links with the modern
world after all. Far to the west one just made out the lights of a
Venezuelan village, while to the distant northeast it was possible to
count flares of waste gas burning at the tips of oil rigs surmounting
underwater wells in the Gulf of Paria. Man continued in his restless, self-advertising ways even here.

Stalking birds with a head lamp is best on a cloudy night and
worst under a full moon, for if a bird can see the stalker behind his
light it may escape capture. This night had been intermediate, for
stars collectively do shed appreciable illumination, however slight.
By working until after ten o'clock, the party had managed to snatch
all the birds they wanted—about 125 of them. Each was placed in
a cloth sack, and the sacks were hung from a wire under a tarpaulin,
to give the bemused tenants plenty of air and to protect them in
case of rain.

I was awake first in the morning, as might be expected. Gradually
the others came to. But no hurried exodus from warm blankets followed. It was too delicious to reach out for thermos flasks of hot
coffee and then watch the sunrise. Someone finally spoiled the fun by
suggesting work. Reluctantly everyone tumbled out, but soon the
routine of banding, bleeding and measuring dispelled memories of

fatigue. Tommy discovered that practically every bird had shed ticks galore into the sacks overnight—in some cases as many as several hundreds from a single captive. This was a real bonus, for now he did not have to collect them arduously, one by one, from underneath stones. The bags were carefully folded, with a notation as to the exact bird each had held, and later at the lab his technicians were assigned the duty of counting them all in their thousands. (The virus again played tricks, for this huge batch of ticks failed to yield it.)

We felt the need to hasten, because the sun soon beat down in tropical fury. For our own welfare it would be good to finish the job, but even more important were the birds, which might suffer heat prostration if not liberated promptly. Thus we finished and broke camp well before noon. Since the boatman had not yet appeared, Richard announced that he would go swimming. I was content to celebrate the occasion by giving the rum bottle a final workout. This was Sunday, and, the Venezuelan pirates being good Roman Catholics, we relaxed in our individual ways without perturbation.

But where was our boatman? A strong wind sprang up from the east late in the morning, and we could see the water becoming rougher by the minute. He arrived about two o'clock, having had engine trouble. We wondered what would have happened if he had been unable to come at all. Our conjecture was that when we failed to turn up at the lab on Monday, Leslie would have called the Coast Guard to come and get us. We must agree on some such arrangement for the future.

Loading the boat was a dangerous and exhausting ordeal, for by this time the waves were so high that the captain did not dare bring his craft in all the way. And once we got out into the bay, away from the lee side of the island, we faced a procession of rollers coming straight at us. These, combined with the wind, slowed us down so that sometimes we seemed to make no progress whatever. The ride was absolutely endless but far from boring, because we had to endure severe torture all the way. The bow of the boat would plow into a great wave, rising up until half the craft had overshot the crest. Then down it would come, bang! into the trough, and our respective bottoms similarly came down, bang! on the hard wooden seats. Poor old Tak had chosen a forward position and took the worst beating. We worried not only about our posteriors but indeed in behalf of our very lives. More than once, home-made Trinidadian boats have broken in two in seas like this. There were no life preservers on board; that was another precaution to be adopted on subsequent trips.

But should we try it again? Perhaps we ought to scratch Soldado Rock from TRVL's agenda. No! The virus cycle must be studied on a year-round basis. Excursions at three-month intervals should suffice for that. I missed some of them when away on other business, but they continued as regularly as the calendar.

The following year we timed a visit to coincide once more with the presence of Sooty Tern chicks. The Rock at night has an utterly different atmosphere when Sooties are there, for their clamor never ceases. Added to that is the fact that they seem to be dominant over Noddies and claim the best places for nesting and roosting. At least those sites seemed best to us, because they coincided with our preference for the saddle. To be sure, a few Noddies managed to establish themselves here, too, but most of them were concentrated on the lower slopes, where eggs and chicks must have more likely chances for dislodgment.

Tommy decided to take four Sooty babies back to the lab for virus inoculation tests, after I assured him that I had once successfully reared an injured young Common Tern in New Jersey. All I had had to do then was buy bait minnows, which the fledgling had gulped in enormous quantities. At the lab in Port-of-Spain we gave the birds a small cage, situated over an enameled pan filled with water to trap any ticks that might fall from them. Any ticks! Each young Sooty Tern dropped almost a thousand during the next five days.

This phenomenon set me off on some calculations that might indicate what the life of a young tern on Soldado Rock must be like. If

one bird is vacated by an average of two hundred ticks per day, it
probably becomes host to two hundred new ones during the same
period. Thus it is constantly parasitized by a population of one
thousand gold diggers. These blood-sucking arthropods may each
remove only one thousandth of a milliliter of blood apiece during
their sojourn, but the result of their concerted feeding must lead
to a loss of one fifth of a milliliter daily. The largest baby
weighed barely 50 grams. Since blood constitutes roughly ten per
cent of the mass of most vertebrate bodies, one can conclude that
this particular bird should own five milliliters of blood, of which
four per cent was being extracted every twenty-four hours. In
smaller babies the drain would be proportionately greater. That
is closely equivalent to a human blood donor's giving one pint
as regularly as sunrise—which no blood bank would countenance.

We often saw dead fledglings on the Rock. Ticks might have been
responsible for some of the fatalities, though of course we could not
tell. I thought that our babies at the lab should thrive, once the last
ectoparasites had left them and reinfestation was precluded. But
they immediately presented a feeding problem. I was able to buy
minnows, but they were frozen. In New Jersey I had bought them
alive, and the Common Tern fledgling apparently recognized them
for what they were by their activity. Thawed minnows at the lab
did not interest sooties at all, and I was forced to push each one
down reluctant throats until an involuntary swallowing reflex was
elicited. Even then the birds often threw up their meals after I
replaced them in the cage.

The recalcitrant captives were nevertheless instructive during
their few weeks of survival. Owing to cramped conditions at the
lab, I was able to give them only two square feet of floor space. Yet
in a couple of days the birds had positioned themselves in definite
territories within that small area. I soon learned to recognize them
individually by minor differences in size, markings and behavior.
Thus, when I came to feed them, I would find each one situated in
a spot that it had adopted for itself, probably not without initial
bickering but at last with communal consent.

Undoubtedly they had responded to one of the instincts that

promotes survival of fledglings in sea-bird colonies. Returning parents, arriving with food, somehow recognize their own young and will not feed babies indiscriminately. But the responsibility—or liability—resides in both camps: chicks also must remain at home where they can be recognized. This seems nonsensical to me, for the flock ought to prosper just as well if everybody fed anyone's children regardless of parentage, but that is not how things work in nature. No doubt our departures from Soldado, after we had mucked everything up with our chasing and herding practices, were marked by hundreds of individual treks as babies returned to their precisely ordained domains of pebbles.

That trip gave us the virus once more—from birds rather than ticks, this time. Now we could revisit the Rock with reduced feelings of professional urgency. However other underlying urges or repulsions remained, especially fear. The next quarterly trip was cancelled by a storm warning, but we felt safe enough a week later. On that very morning another storm brewed, but we decided to go anyhow, for TRVL's calendar said we must. This Saturday we were Tommy, Richard, Elisha, and Charlie Collins, a graduate student from the University of Florida, currently making ornithological studies at Simla in the Arima Valley. (I shall have more to report about Charlie.)

At Cedros, while we were loading the boat, a kindly policeman informed us that the radio was broadcasting hourly warnings from the Coast Guard and Weather Bureau, advising all small craft to remain ashore. He had no authority to prevent our embarkation, so we put it up to the boatman. In his opinion the storm had already passed, for the water had been much rougher earlier, and someone had merely neglected to tell the radio people to discontinue their automatic tape recording. The sea *was* smooth, and we had a serene ride to Soldado.

As usual, I went to bed early and the others followed after their labors were finished. Then the first large drop splashed on my face. Frigatebirds had been sleeping overhead, and I suspected that this might not be rain. However when I opened my eyes I found that stars had been obscured and it was so dark that it was impossible to know whether frigatebirds were still up there or not. Another drop, and another. "A passing shower," I thought, and pulled the blanket over my head.

Now the rain pelted down. Soon the blanket was saturated. Well, I had slept out in rain before, and in the tropics body heat often serves to make even a wet shroud not too uninhabitable. But I had forgotten to reckon with the canvas cot. This admirable article of field equipment is designed to be waterproof, and so it was. It refused to allow water to drain through its closely woven fabric, and soon I was lying in a miniature swimming pool.

At approximately the same moment that I decided something must be done and popped my head out from under the soggy blanket, other heads popped out, too. "Wide awake!" shouted Elisha. One by one we upended cots to empty them and wrung out blankets, though that was a useless reflex action.

What can you do under such circumstances except dwell on your misery? Tommy, bless him, knew the precise answer. "Let's play word games," he suggested. "First we'll play 'Rivers, Cities and Countries.' I'll begin: O.K., 'Afghanistan.' Your turn, Richard—your letter is 'N.' "

So it rained and so we played through the night. Five o'clock brought a slight remission in the deluge, by which time Elisha was no longer responding to calls for his next turn. He was slumped against a tiny outcrop of rock that sheltered an incubating noddy at his elbow. The rest of us had run out of names but had begun to fabricate them for the sake of endurance. "Don't you suppose there may be a place somewhere called Dartmouthsdorp?" asked Charlie.

Winds diminished, clouds blew away, and the sun came up in splendor. Like drenched vultures, we spread ourselves to its rays, and like them we soon found capable wings for our work. But as we left Soldado that time, I resolved to consign the project to younger hands. Charlie, for example, was inspired as I might have been one generation previously. Finding a partially mummified frigatebird carcass, he insisted on bringing it back as a valuable trophy, smell and all. "It will make a splendid skeleton," he protested over our protests.

That indeed was my last trip, but only in part because of faint heart. Virus studies had now reached a reasonably satisfactory stage, and TRVL policy decreed that further investigations could be made less routinely, if at all. Meanwhile I had found a contact with ornithologists in Jamaica who were banding Noddies and Sooty Terns on the Morant Cays off the southeast coast of that Caribbean island. Wouldn't this be a perfect place to establish a link between ticks, birds and viruses between Key West and Trinidad? I returned from the Jamaican visit full of enthusiasm for Tommy's future participation in a new project.

"Well," said Tommy laconically.

That was sufficient: it meant "Yes."

Chapter 11

THE ARIMA VALLEY

*C*harlie Collins can talk anyone into anything. At least he overwhelmed me with conversation, and I suppose he must have other victims by the score. Not that I minded—I liked it—but he got me into a couple of messes, simply because I resigned myself to his verbosity. That mummified frigatebird from Soldado Rock contributed to spectacular consequences of my weakness in the river of his unquenchable flow of words.

"Since you are about to attend the annual meeting of the American Ornithologists' Union in Lawrence, Kansas," Charlie said, "of course you'll not mind taking the carcass with you and presenting it to my friend, Dr. Robert Storer, of Ann Arbor, Michigan, who will be everlastingly grateful to you for acting as messenger boy. Skeletons of frigatebirds are almost nonexistent in collections—yet they have inestimable value as teaching models. Take swifts and hummingbirds—they have tremendously developed keels on their breastbones: the proportions can be linked with function and such physical attributes as weight, wing length and rapidity of flight. Frigatebirds, on the other hand, are at the other extreme. Their relatively tiny breastbones——"

"O.K., Charlie," I said in defeat, "I'll take the stinking thing to Dr. Storer." Which I did, while experiencing formidable heart

attacks occasioned by conscientious and totally laudable agents of
the U.S. Bureau of Entomology and Plant Quarantine at Miami
Airport. First I presented my ordinary and innocent luggage to
the polite Customs inspector. But then there was that large card-
board container, marked with large letters, "Scientific specimen: no
commercial value."

"What's in it?" he asked.

"A dried-up bird," I answered.

Since the first days of this century, when a ban was placed on the
importation of feathers of wild birds for the female millinery trade,
our Customs people have been more conscientious about contra-
band birds than any other article, unless it was liquor during the
era of Prohibition. One can get permits for bona fide importations
—to zoos and museums, for example—but this was not quite that
official. Besides, my intention was to pass it off as a skeleton only,
in which case the law did not apply.

My man got his hackles up at once. "Wait till I call one of the
Plant Quarantine agents," he ordered.

The new, blue-uniformed inspector listened to my tale but ended
up with one insistent question: "Has it got feathers on it?"

Frankly, I did not know. When Charlie picked it up on Soldado
Rock, it surely did—plus significant portions of rotting soft tissue.
Now, in its wrappings, the specimen was devoid of perceptible
exhalations. Perhaps he had cleaned it up and the parcel truly
contained no more than bones. I had not had a chance to quiz him:
on one of his trips to Port-of-Spain he left it, fully sealed, on my
desk, where I found it when I returned from Bush Bush.

There was nothing to do in Miami but open the box and look.
There lay the mummy, fully clothed in every feather it had possessed in life! I learned later that Charlie had simply baked it in a
drying oven for botanical specimens until the job begun originally
by the sun reached completion.

Now I was on my mettle both as an exposed smuggler, hoping to
escape the consequences, and as a champion of Dr. Storer's teaching
needs. "Look," I said, "these feathers don't count at all. As I have
already explained to the first gentleman, this entire mess will be

immersed in a bath of alkali until digestion removes every scrap of dried flesh, sinew, internal organs—indeed all parts except calcified ones. Feathers obviously will be the first to go. The final product will be a nice, clean skeleton that can be put together by one of our future ornithologists as part of his graduate training."

The blue-suited man appeared to be slightly moved. "What kind of a bird is it?" he wanted to know. Now things began to shape up a bit more in my favor. It seemed he was a fisherman and had often seen frigatebirds—"Man-o'-war Birds," as he called them—at a distance, for this species occurs as far north as southern Florida. The conversation then went on to pelicans, and first thing I knew he had been converted to Dr. Storer's side.

I went on happily to Lawrence, Kansas, but now I had to identify the appropriate human being. I finally met him, along with several dozens of other human life listers. Though I thought I had fixed him in my mind, something slipped. Returning to my room in the U. of Kansas dormitory one evening, I thought I spotted him down the hall. Seizing the opportunity, I called, "Come along here for a few minutes—we'll have some Trinidadian rum and I'll give you your Man-o'-War." "The visit will be splendid," said Dr. Alden H. Miller, (now deceased), of California, "but I don't understand the rest of your offer."

At the A.O.U. registration desk I learned (at last) the number of Bob Storer's room. On the final afternoon of the meeting I knocked on his door. To my consternation it was opened by an attractive lady in a negligee. Thrusting the carton into her hands, I blurted, "Here's a dead bird for your mummy," and ran.

That's what Charlie Collins can do to you. Yet my story of the Magnificent Frigatebird has a purpose beyond praise for that admirable young friend. I can't even use him as a prototype of all the naturalists who occupied the Arima Valley, for they were individualists in the extreme sense. However, one trait they shared: to them natural history was an occupation and avocation in and for itself, without trappings of applied science. Having been nurtured at Swarthmore College in that same pure, academic atmosphere, before becoming contaminated with miasmas rising from more worldly aspects of dollar expenditures, I found the Valley an oasis. For some reason that I cannot explain, I rarely went there. Perhaps I was too busy. But I felt comforted at all times by the realization that only a few miles away, within ready reach, were people to whom I could address a language that once I had known more fluently.

The center of that congregation was Simla, the field station of the New York Zoological Society. This had been established and donated to the Society a decade previously by the late famed Dr. C. William Beebe, who was still present when I came to Trinidad, although greatly enfeebled. His voice had been reduced to a whisper by a respiratory infection, but that malady had by no means touched his mind. Once I arrived with a black eye acquired in an accident and he came up with "Beefsteak!" On another occasion I was admiring an entire shelf of his books—about twenty of them. His remark then was "Potboilers!" Although his nature writing has been acclaimed by reputable critics, he deprecated these books for having popular appeal rather than containing scientific sawdust. By his own admission he wrote each one to finance the next expedition. His scheme worked for a lifetime, to the great advantage of the New York Zoological Society and a procession of younger naturalists who came to Simla to study tropical flora and fauna.

I had read several of Dr. Beebe's books as a younger man and found them inspiring. In them he often mentioned a youthful female naturalist, Jocelyn Crane, who accompanied most of his sorties and was apparently an expert on marine invertebrates. Well, here she was at Simla, too, looking after her aged mentor as devotedly as a daughter. But how could she study oceanic life on the jungled slope of a tropical hillside? There are two answers to that. First, you can build a salt-water pool and populate it with fiddler crabs from the nearby coast. Second, you can unbend and turn your attention to butterflies. She had done both.

Joss acted as a most gracious hostess at Simla, and the wonder is that she had time left for any work at all. She had to attend to the housekeeping and to the special needs of each arriving scholar.

Then, too, there was an entertainment schedule, for Simla is totally isolated, without a telephone and devoid of electricity not generated on the premises, and morale was immensely benefited by a gay party now and then. These began with "Simla Specials" on a lovely stone-flagged terrace and progressed to a sumptuous pilau or curry at candlelit tables indoors.

Dr. Donald Griffin, formerly at Harvard and now at the new Rockefeller University in New York, was an annual winter visitor, and he always entertained us at the cocktail hour with demonstrations of his "echo-location machine"—I don't know what else to call it. As dusk fell and we sipped our drinks, bats came out for their evening breakfasts, and Don was able to pick up their cruising and hunting voices with an ingenious electronic contrivance. Bats emit bursts of sound that are too high-pitched for the human ear to catch, but this device somehow converted them to a lower frequency. Don would point a microphone, resembling the baton of an orchestra leader, at a passing bat, and out of the loud-speaker came a steady series of clicks. Suddenly the clicks became faster; we would see the bat swerve; and in a crescendo of clicks the bat would complete one of its aerial gymnastics. Don could actually keep a sort of score. "It caught that one," he might say. Or, "Missed that time." When Don began his studies, it seemed incredible that bats might be able to locate flying insects and judge the prey's diminishing distance by appreciating shortened times required for echoes of their own voices to return to their ears, but now he had established the fact so thoroughly that it ranked as preprandial amusement more than scientific demonstration.

These were the kinds of people one met at Simla. Not a virologist in the lot! Indeed, they were *against* virologists in general, for they knew too well that we of TRVL were trapping and slaughtering all sorts of wildlife in our pursuit of human welfare. One rigid rule at Simla is: "Observe, but do not collect." However, that maxim can be interpreted variously. "Temporary captivity" may be regarded as within the law, according to what practices will befall the incarcerated creatures. Jocelyn's butterfly studies, for example, became involved with the problem of a young ornithologist who wanted to discover whether fledgling birds know instinctively that certain butterflies are distasteful or whether they have to find it out through nasty personal experience. Since she was already raising the appropriate butterflies in several screened outdoor insectaria— repugnant ones and their tasty mimics, as well as species in each category that would be unlikely to cause confusion—permission was granted for the ornithologist to search for birds' nests and remove babies just when they were about to fly. Joss, having known of the impending project for a year, had raised butterflies like mad and stored a great stock of them in a deep freeze. Unfortunately I can't report what happened, except that the birds were released afterwards. But I wonder how "uncollected" they really were. At the precise stage when they should have been learning to make their own way, self-education was interrupted by an extremely artificial experience while their butterfly reactions were being observed surreptitiously through one-way window glass. Maybe, being highly automatic and unintelligent in their reactions, they simply waited in the bush for further offerings of butterflies to be poked at them.

Some scientists at Simla chafed at nature-loving restrictions, because of the peculiar requirements of their specialties. If, for example, an individual is wedded to curiosity about the comparative structure of livers or kidneys of differing vertebrates, he can't surmise anything by watching lizards, rodents and birds in the field or in cages. These people occasionally ended up at TRVL, and usually they made inordinate demands on us. Almost invariably they wanted the most esoteric creatures on the island, forms of which we felt ourselves lucky to have even a single specimen in our little museum—after ten years of devoted field work. Naturally we were glad to accommodate requests for common material; I could easily ask Bertie Sam to pick out a couple of Zygos or *Oryzomys* of the desired age and sex. But as for silky anteaters, for instance, I once saw Wil Downs almost blow his top though he is normally receptive to requests that I might consider outrageous.

I approved of Simla's policy, which was really Will Beebe's original dictum. Because of it, the old man in his eighties was able to sit and admire a wilderness that he considered unspoiled. Perhaps he realized that it was not a totally natural scene, but at least he was an agent in preventing the environment from deteriorating further. A magnificent sight at one time each year was the flowering of immortelle trees to the north. Entire series of hills were then clad in pink, as if the forest were composed of only this one kind of tree. Will looked forward to that season and exulted in it. But what is an immortelle other than a quickly growing shade tree for cocoa and coffee? And how can immortelles thrive unless the original forest has been cut down first?

These questions troubled me in Trinidad, and they still do. When you fly over the Northern Range, the slopes appear to be clad with primeval jungle, the tops of trees forming a solid canopy. On the contrary, if you walk through those forests, it is unusual, except at the highest peaks of land, to come upon a stand of timber that does not show the gnawing effects of some preceding human being. Just when you think you have reached a real retreat from civilization, you are accosted by a spindly, struggling cocoa tree, overshadowed today by forest giants that are not immortelles, which attests to former cultivation of the area. I guess one must go to the Amazon for really immaculate experience.

Further evidence of total human occupation includes the present day. Crowning forest trees bespeak Trinidad's wise conservation of its watershed, but a continuing, regulated harvest of lumber and crops continues. The hinterlands, far beyond roads accessible by cars or trucks, are peopled by a largely illiterate gentry who adhere to solitude and silviculture in one form or another. Those who do not hew trees, under government permits, tend cocoa groves under a similar license. The Range is crisscrossed by trails accessible to the feet of human beings, donkeys and bullocks. Occasionally one comes upon imprints of derelict bicycle wheels on most unlikely forest paths.

I have two approaches to shrouded wildernesses. The first one necessarily takes in everything—a collective conglomeration of endless tall trunks, massive branches forming a canopy, and the sundry lesser shrubs and tree ferns that form a stage on which larger actors stand frozen but seemingly alert. The assemblage conveys one generic impression: jungle! And to assimilate it fully, one must *not* see the trees for the forest. To do so would be to lose the entire mood of this place—its very atmosphere in a literal sense—for the air has a special feel and conducts light in a special way, so that all vistas, as one slowly dawdles along a trail, clearly belong to the same family.

Delightful as that sort of perception is, I am unable to indulge such aesthetic responsiveness except in spurts. The first thing I know, I am looking at a *single* tree, and then the jungle collapses. Gone are the cloisters and their misty arches. Here is a person to know, like my avocado pet in Port-of-Spain.

Usually my attention has been kidnaped by that ever-fascinating drama of struggle between an independent monarch and a strangler fig. One has learned that only seven or so basic plots exist in human storytelling, but the situations in which strangler figs can dispose themselves for our reading are endless. I suppose the reason is that the rational human mind will accept only reasonable propositions: a real king riding into battle on a real mouse, for example, makes no sense to us, and in fantasy remains almost as ludicrous.

But that—and more bizarre miscasting—can be seen every day in the strangler fig's world. Fruits of this clasper are eaten by birds, seeds being then distributed in their droppings. Who knows where those progeny will fall? I do: everywhere! That is why so many sproutings of baby figs are crazy and only a few are opportune— for the fig, that is. As for trees, they should applaud every bird that drops a seed where it hasn't got a chance.

Ideally the young plant should find itself in a crotch about half- way up an immature tree having a diameter of no more than one foot. When its groping roots finally reach the ground and begin to expand, they will have a sensible chance of embracing the trunk until they engulf the entire bole and henceforth support their own crown. Meanwhile the host tree will have died, so that the fig need no longer compete with alien leaves for sunshine.

That is the perfect sequence. In contrast, one usually sees fig seed- lings that struggle in impossible situations. If the victimized tree happens to be already mature, fig rootlets can never encompass it

to form a sheath. Sometimes they succeed in weaving a tangle of intertwining cords about the trunk; otherwise they may simply descend straight to the ground like metal cables; but the giant is not discomfited in either case.

When individual trees invite reveries that become too absorbing, it is wise to return to the car and drive a bit farther. Even at slow speed one dare not allow the eye to become fixed. By means of this trick I used to bring myself back to the Arima Valley at large. Having left Simla behind at the four-mile post, I thus came eventually to the entrance of Spring Hill Estate near the eight-mile post, though the sharp windings of the narrow Blanchisseuse Road, upward through ravine after ravine, made the distance seem much greater.

Here was Mrs. Asa Wright's run-down cocoa plantation and her haven for paying-guest naturalists. These were an entirely different breed from incumbents at Simla, for they came to Asa's not so much to make studies that would be reported later in scientific journals but chiefly to enjoy themselves. Not that the Simla people weren't happy or that Asa's guests were oblivious to science; the two groups simply approached the same subjects in different ways.

The "run-down" condition of this plantation resulted from Asa's no longer being able to supervise her men vigorously. But in a wry way she reaped a reverse benefit from the laborers' lack of love for labor: the more overgrown and unkempt her sloping acres became, the more they were repopulated by indigenous forest birds and wildlife. Her "trade" in naturalists would never have been as successful in a well-tended plantation. As it was, she placed a few ads in *Audubon Magazine* and similar media, and the first few comers to spend a number of days or weeks at Spring Hill quickly spread news of its wonders by word of mouth.

Asa would sweep me into her great bear hug, introduce me to whoever was there, invite me to have coffee, and then lead me to her screened veranda overlooking the valley. Here we shouted at each other, both being deaf, but not so stridently that I could not hear the Mossy-throated Bellbirds far below. "Tock, tock, tock-tock-tock," came the strange *un*-bell-like voice of a perched male, proclaiming his territory, and, "Tock, tock, tock-tock-tock," responded a more distant, also stationary, voice.

These birds—black-and-white males and brown-and-white females—are cotingas, members of a strangely assorted family that is confined to the Western Hemisphere and almost entirely to the American tropics, although one smallish species, the Rose-throated Becard, creeps across the Mexican border into our southwestern states in two or three places. Bellbirds are the size of Blue Jays, and some of the South American forms utter truly bell-like notes that carry far through the forest.

David and Barbara Snow, who were attached to Simla for four years (largely before my advent), made unexcelled studies of Mossy-throated Bellbirds in the Arima Valley. They were able to net a few and band them with plastic rings of different colors so that individuals could be recognized later through binoculars, obviating the need for further recaptures. In addition they watched the birds so assiduously that they finally knew where each male maintained its set of calling perches; even banding became largely superfluous. As with the little manakins, courtship in bellbirds does not require pursuit of females but simply masculine self-advertisement. Males mark out their separate areas for calling and females resort to spouses of their own selection. What the function of the "mossy throat" may be, no one knows. Certainly females are attracted first by voice; it is only after close approach that they could inspect a potential husband's beard of curious, multiple, inch-long wattles, looking like thin strands of black rubber. But by then a female would probably be beyond retreating.

The habits of most tropical birds are so little understood that even amateur ornithologists can easily make original observations. The Snows, however, were professionals, which is why their combined studies were so highly enlightening. To cite one more instance: they wanted to know what bellbirds eat. I would consider this an impossible assignment when it concerns a shy, jungle-dwelling species. But David and Barbara spread burlap sacks, old tarpaulins and other scraps of cloth under the calling perches of several male bellbirds, and over the years they made endless collections of everything that accumulated on those surfaces. Whether fecal droppings or indigestible regurgitations, these objects— mainly seeds—spelled out the bellbird diet for every month of the year, in accord with seasonal blossoming and fruiting of multitudes of forest trees.

Asa Wright was fortunate to have bellbirds on her property, for these are distributed only locally in the Northern Range. Besides, they are among the "greats" that American birders want to see. But she had another attraction, even more alluring, and it is to her credit that she had preserved it, long before having to resort to paying guests for ancillary income.

The real thriller was a colony of Oilbirds. These bizarre, pigeon-sized, nocturnal creatures, with speckled chocolate plumage and owl-like heads, are related to nightjars—or, if you will, goatsuckers —including our often heard but rarely seen Whip-poor-will. They live by day in caves, where they not only perch on high ledges when idle but also construct their mud nests. Babies hatch in these clammy nurseries, naked and helpless. Parents forage for fruits of various forest trees at night so efficiently that progeny soon become excessively fat. Primitive peoples collect the chicks for that reason. In South America they have been used not only for food but for lamp fuel.

Oilbird caves, found only in Trinidad, Venezuela and Peru, are usually inaccessible to all but the most daring and energetic ornithologists, but Asa Wright's colony at Spring Hill was exceptional for being situated in a narrow, irregular cleft between two huge rocks. A stream ran between cliff faces, and one could wade through a series of pools and freshets to the nesting area, where a bit of light still filtered through the narrow overhead fissure. Many visitors to Trinidad have added Asa's Oilbirds to their life lists.

Not more than a dozen pairs resided here. David Snow made a study of their diets, similar to his bellbird investigation, by affixing pieces of screen wire below the nesting ledges, to catch fruit pits and other large seeds spilled from above. By such means he discovered a species of jungle tree hitherto unknown in Trinidad. Indeed his finding led first to speculation that our local Oilbirds might

forage at night in Venezuela, all the way across the Gulf of Paria.
But the disclosure was soon followed by intensified searches which
led the Forestry Department to establish the unsuspected presence
of this tree not far from Spring Hill.

In contrast to Asa Wright's small gathering of Oilbirds, the Aripo
Cave, in another valley to the east, was occupied by several hundreds. That colony was far more typical, both as to its populousness
and the effort required to reach it. One had to walk for a few miles
over rough terrain, after the auto road through the Northern Range
came to an end, to a spot where a stream came gushing out of the
mountainside. Sloshing into the aperture, one soon lost sight of the
entrance but continued battling the current upstream by the light
of a head lamp. The rocky stream bed was slippery underfoot, the
chilly water hideously cold up to the waist, and the lowering ceiling
of the tunnel forced one's bent head and shoulders almost into
swirling waters. Should a heavy mountain shower suddenly raise the
level of this flood, one might be doomed.

In total blackness the adit opened onto a vast cavern. Now our
unwonted lights aroused bedlam. We were in the sanctum of *two*
echo-locating forms of life—multitudes of bats of several kinds and
the extraordinary Oilbird, which is the only avian creature known
to have developed a kind of sonar as a means of navigation in complete darkness. The bats were thoughtful of our ears; Don Griffin
had already demonstrated the need for a sophisticated electronic
box to transform their cries to a range within human hearing. Unfortunately—or perhaps it is our good fortune to be attracted by
the unusual—Oilbirds sense sounds the way we do, and their
vocal search for echoes from cave walls impinged on our delicate
tympani horrendously. There is no reason why they should have
used a scale familiar to lovers of opera or the symphony; that
would have been too extraordinary. But why their departure from
harmonic intervals should have extended to such outlandish—by
our standards—eerie shrieks and groans, just to find their normal
emotional outlets, escapes my comprehension. Part of their babble
was necessary routine. As they flew about, one could distinguish
clacks of different frequencies that must have been flight guides,

OILBIRD

for they had every suggestion of being businesslike. Almost drowning those out, however, were curdling vociferations uttered from rock ledges. Cave walls multiplied every sound, until one almost reeled in a circumambient din.

Our lights disclosed hordes of silent bats that had come down from roosts in clouds. *Their* sonar, not benefiting by Don's machine, was insensible to us on this occasion but it served them traditionally, for not one of the throng collided with us, even in spite of the possibly confusing beams of head lamps.

In this cave, one is surrounded by so many birds that it is difficult to estimate their numbers except in terms of scores or fifties. Light beams can take in only a tiny sector of the environment at one time. Meanwhile birds are flying everywhere in short sallies, now brushing past in raucous consternation, again returning to overhead crevices. Untold pairs of eyes glow like illuminated rubies from those retreats, providing one means for counting some of the denizens.

It is remarkable that the initial flight of a fledged Oilbird must be made in total blackness. This means that its voice and ears must now be as fully developed as the skeleton, muscles and feathers. Perhaps babies become so fat because it is necessary for them to remain in their nests longer than most other young birds, in order to achieve greater maturity before venturing on that first stygian take-off. Even so, one wonders what proportion of them is lost at the opening of flying school. The fact that Oilbirds may lay as many as four eggs suggests that at some stage the species suffers a significant mortality that demands compensation. Birds with high chances for survival of their young—penguins and auks, for example—usually produce only one at a time. However, this reflection must be extended also to mortality rates among adult birds, so the matter is not as simple as one might think. Species with a life expectancy of twenty years can afford to lose more broods than creatures whose span of breeding is limited to a mere two or three seasons. Thus many short-lived small birds lay large clutches of eggs even when fledging success is of a fairly high order. Obviously Oilbirds deserve the attention of more David Snows and fewer life-list addicts.

Chapter 12

SPIDERS AND BUGS

Leon could cook, but he was not trained as a house servant. That suited me perfectly, for if he had been the perfect cleaner and valet he would not have allowed me to maintain part of the squalor that made my life interesting. A nest of house mice in the pocket of my woolen bathrobe in a closet was suffered to remain there until baby mice made their way out of doors and the bathrobe had been chewed to rags. But most holy of all: cobwebs in my study must never be brushed away, for their architects were my best friends.

Already I have cast a slur on those companions. "Cobwebs" is what a housewife would surely have called their homes, but these structures were "orbs." Until I learned a bit of spider lore, I had always thought that an orb was a globe of some kind—certainly a three-dimensional object. Looking into the matter, I learned that "orb" is a perfectly proper word for things such as wheels. Even without spokes, "orb" can apply to the plane surface marked out by a revolving satellite like our earth in its course around the sun: hence the term, "orbit."

Orb-weaving spiders come in great variety, but not many of them invade houses. Mostly they frequent open situations where rapidly flying insects are likely to impinge on their webs. One can find them commonly in gardens, overgrown fields, hedgerows and woods. Because their prey may be either large or quickly moving, orb weavers spin strong, sticky webs. The spokes of the "wheel" have great tensile strength, while the spiral strands connecting radii are dotted with mucilaginous droplets. An insect therefore first strikes the trampoline, but instead of bouncing out it is held by glue. Ever-ready spiders rush at once to the spot to immobilize the captive before it can break away. They do this by first enmeshing it in further webbing, secreted on the instant, and then injecting poison from their fangs.

Perhaps orb weavers don't sound like nice friends. Quite to the contrary, the ones I admired and protected have already proved inoffensive and valuable to mankind. I did not know that at first, but Tommy happened to show me an article which told everything I wanted to know. These arachnids, about an inch long between tips of front and hind legs, are called tropicopolitan spiders, *Uloborus geniculatus*, and have actually been encouraged in tobacco warehouses for their usefulness in destroying cigarette beetles.

They were useful enough to me just as entertainers. To begin with, their webs were strikingly attractive, for at the center of each one the resident spun a lacy doily upon which it sat. Most often, spiders faced upwards with their two front legs held together, as if pointing to twelve o'clock. For a while I thought they always did this, but then I began to observe individuals that favored any time of day.

Seen under a lens, the tropicopolitan spider is an entrancing being. Its eight legs are not merely mottled black and white as they appear to an unaided eye. Instead, they are marked off into alternating segments of stygian opacity and glassy transparence. I must interpolate a remark here about entomologists and their hand lenses. These optical aids are acknowledged needs for their profession, because most insects are so tiny, but they are also means for entering a world of beauty that largely escapes the rest of us. Even if one is not an entomologist and hates bugs, a lens will reveal forms and colors that could inspire poetry and art. A magnification of only five diameters is sufficient for a shattering introduction to the entomological world. I don't like "hand" lenses that tie up fifty per cent of your fingers; I use either a 5x jeweler's glass with a steel spring that extends to the back of the head or a binocular "Optivisor," with a complete elastic headband (such as "invisible mending" people employ in repairing cigarette burns in best suits after parties).

A lens adds to the fun but is not essential. Against the windows of my study, spiders gave me daily note of what was going on simply as I glanced at them while approaching or leaving my desk. Here one was sucking a freshly caught fly. There a brood of babies had just hatched. Elsewhere a fat mother was weaving a cocoon for forthcoming eggs.

Those cocoons were among the most lovely biological creations I have seen. With Optivisor or naked eye, I could appreciate them as lavender-colored stellate purses. One point of the star was always a bit broader than the remaining four or five, providing an escape tunnel for spiderlings.

I felt almost as if I should rescue each egg case before hatching occurred, for cannibalistic mothers might not make appropriate discrimination between baby footfalls in the web and legitimate small prey. However, Nature took care of that. Females remained in a protective role until progeny emerged from lavender-colored shrouds, but then they abandoned the web to the new generation. That afforded little inconvenience to mothers, at the same time giving infants a great opportunity to get into the swing of things.

Limited food supply in the study was the only curb to the room's becoming one solid mass of flytraps. Some windows were constantly open, though I reserved special closed ones for spiders even on hot days when more ventilation would have been welcome. Thus it was a matter of chance whether an insect, having flown into the house, escaped through an open window or flew against glass panes—and then usually into a web. Since the number of successful collisions—from the spiders' point of view—was fairly constant most of the time, an increasing number of spiders was incompatible with the basic economy. I think some of the newcomers may have found their way outside, but cannibalism probably accounted for the greater part of population control. That this did not take place at birth is undoubtedly a factor in species survival, for such a practice would lead to self-extinction. But soon after birth, each individual must fear its own kind.

Egg cases yielded an average of twenty-four babies. Within very few days one would be able to count only twenty, then fifteen, and so on. Judging from their distribution close to the maternal web, I suspected that this critical cannibalism was among the babies. As the decreasing number of survivors went through successive molts, becoming larger after each ecdysis, they spread farther apart, encroaching on territories occupied by adults. Now they became prey of their mothers and aunts. Of the original twenty-four, only enough attained adulthood to replace losses of long-established grown-ups— grandparents, perhaps.

Maternal behavior, which I could scrutinize in front of my nose on study windows, gave me a clue to what happened to another orb-weaving mother at We House. This was a gigantic spider whose name I never learned. The span of her legs must have been close to four inches. Her fat abdomen was oddly molded, being about twice as long as broad and definitely humpbacked. When I add that this abdomen was green with a sprinkling of yellow polka dots, and that the joints of the legs bore tufts of blackish hairs, you can realize what an attractive creature this was.

The web was spun under one of the eaves of We House, near the "bee box," which I shall describe later. Indeed, bees may have attracted the spider in the first place, for she proceeded to catch numbers of them in her two-foot snare. Again I was interested in both sides and therefore admonished Leon not to disturb the situation, even though the bees really belonged to him and Motilal.

But the matter took care of itself. After several weeks, the spider spun a large golden cocoon against the side of the house and disappeared. At first I wondered what had befallen her, for the web remained intact. Then I began putting two and two together and decided that here was another example of a maternal spider that would automatically devour her brood if she remained on hand.

On a return visit not long thereafter I observed that the eggs had hatched, for the wall of the cocoon was studded with chalky egg-shells. Curious to learn how the case had been constructed, I tore it from the wall and began to rip it apart. To my amazement, I found it crammed with babies. Apparently they had simply gotten rid of the shells and then resealed themselves in the cradle. And well they might have done so, for my Optivisor revealed them as still being soft, pallid things in no condition to charge into a hostile jungle.

Now I was in a quandary. To fasten the cocoon in its original position on the wall was one obvious step to take, but I was afraid that my house-wrecking might expose the babies to predators. I elected instead to drop the case into a jar, cover over the top with mosquito netting, and place it on the work table indoors where I could watch it. But I need not have worried—the babies soon closed the rent with silk, and the cocoon continued on its inert career.

On reflection, I was glad to have taken this treasure captive, for I would now be assured of learning at least one sequel. I had seen that the cocoon was crowded with small babies—hundreds of them. Should hundreds eventually emerge, I could conclude that their waiting period after hatching but before stepping forth into the world was merely a needed interval required for the hardening of their cuticular exoskeletons. But if only a few *larger* spiders appeared, it would prove that cannibalism and early molting inside the home was an alternative pathway to preparation for coping with the perils of extreme infancy. Might it not be more efficient to sacrifice part of the brood, in order to launch limited numbers of hardier individuals, than to risk the whole population at birth?

I must confess relief when, a week later, I found the jar swarming with spiderlings, possibly as many as five hundred. Moreover they were the same size as those I had observed in the cocoon, so cannibalism could be dismissed. In addition, their abdomens had darkened. Thus the first hypothesis, regarding a resting period while some degree of maturation occurred, must be correct. I noticed something else, too: just as all human babies have button noses, even when their parents have hawk beaks, so the spiderlings' abdomens were perfectly rotund, giving no suggestion of their future humpbacked and elongated configurations.

They had already filled the jar with webbing, about which they clambered at random. Now it was time to set them free. I was glad for a second time that I had incarcerated the cocoon, because the babies would now teach me how they go about dispersing themselves. I placed the jar at the base of a small sapling and removed its cover, at which stimulus the horde came clambering out with leggy confusion.

Soon another conundrum presented itself. All the spiders climbed to the same spot on the sapling and began to spin. Were they acting independently but impelled by identical instincts, or did this represent a temporary sort of juvenile colonialism? I came to accept the latter hypothesis, for by the next day they had moved to a higher branch, still as a group, although there were numerous diverging pathways along which they could have split their numbers.

The joint web they had spun was not an orb—or a multiplicity of orbs—in any sense. It was, rather, a three-dimensional mass of strands, about ten inches in diameter, that gave footing to a spider almost anywhere it might choose to locate itself. And what a pretty ballet they performed! Though constantly moving slowly as individuals, their community maintained a balanced disklike stance with a great concentration of members at the center and with gradually diminishing outliers peripherally. It was not fanciful to think of them as a stellar galaxy.

But that was the end of that—next week there was no sign of them, not even the web. However, I feel that all was well. Even if an antbird or a wren had attacked that celestial society—and it would have been a rich feast for any hungry bird—some of the stars would have fallen and escaped. More likely the babies had completed a few more hours or days of "hardening" and then set out on solitary orbits.

I used to ponder on many of these unavoidable gaps in my information while occupied near We House in the latrine, that bucolic structure so admirably celebrated by James Whitcomb Riley for its invitations to contemplation. Here I had long become familiar with another type of spider, which spun true cobwebs of the most untidy kind. These arachnids looked not only uninteresting but also unattractive, resembling a daddy-longlegs more than anything else, with small, shrunken bodies and long, thin legs spanning between two and three inches.

One morning after breakfast I was watching them idly, when "a new planet swam into my ken." Tommy had told me ages ago that an extremely peculiar kind of South American bug, inhabiting spiderwebs, was reputed to exist also in Trinidad, though in his years as an entomologist on the island he had never seen one. However that was no slur on Tommy's qualities as an observer, for he showed me the letter he had received from Professor Robert Usinger of Berkeley, California, urging him to look for such bugs and stating that "they are scarce as hens' teeth." In addition the letter gave the bugs the name of *Arachnicorus,* i.e., "spider affiliated," and that is all the information we had.

Of course, when an entomologist uses the term "bug," that is exactly what he means—not just any insect but a member of the particular order—Hemiptera (or Hemiptera and Homoptera)— containing "true" bugs. Consequently Tommy and I could look into spiderwebs with somewhat sharpened skill: we would not be fooled by winged termites or blundering beetles that might have been temporarily impeded in a web. Mosquitoes, moreover, often rest by design on abandoned cobwebs, so that the quest (in which Tommy at once enlisted me) required at least rudimentary abilities to discriminate.

As I casually watched the spiders in the latrine on this morning, for perhaps the hundredth time, I became aware of a small antlike creature near the fringe of one of the messy webs. Mind you, Tommy and I didn't even know what *Arachnicorus* looks like— whether large, medium or tiny, or whether broad, narrow, brilliant, dull or any of the other qualities one could name. But here was a being that electrified my comprehension in a twinkling—it must be

Arachnicorus, for it was doing the impossible, sedately treading the web as if walking on water.

I rushed to We House for the Optivisor and soon had my "hen's tooth" in magnified view. No doubt about its being a true bug: there was the long, sucking proboscis tucked down between its legs against the thorax. Also two pairs of membranous wings. Also everything else about it was buglike, though it was itself a most unspectacular member of its order, generally resembling some creeping ground insect: narrowness of the inconspicuous wings intensified that similarity.

A physician observing me from that day on would have concluded that I was suffering from a most virulent or chronic form of tropical dysentery. I ran out to the latrine constantly to see what was going on, for after I had learned to recognize *Arachnicorus,* I discovered that the webs were loaded with them. Well, perhaps loaded is too strong a word, but if a creature is supposed to be rare, and you ascertain by repeated censuses that you have thirty-eight of them under surveillance within a small wooden structure, you rather feel that your hen has acquired a generous set of dentures.

The next question was: to collect or not to collect? Instinctively I decided that the biology of these bugs must be unknown; if they were so sparsely represented in museum trays (which is what Professor Usinger meant), no one was likely to have studied them afield. I could immediately have made thirty-eight entomologists wildly happy by collecting the whole population and sending each scientist a perfect specimen. But that would not have added anything intellectual to human lore. No, I must make the latrine my abode, adhering to James Whitcomb Riley's counsel. (Indeed, Wysten Auden has very recently given us similar sober advice.)

This admirable course yielded disappointing results. The trouble was that the bugs rarely *did* anything. After all, I was doing my regular work, and I popped into the latrine only briefly from time to time. Invariably I would find each bug close to where it had been before. I could not learn whether they and the spiders were friends, enemies or simply indifferent to each other. What the bugs ate remained a mystery. And where were baby bugs? Did they hatch from eggs laid elsewhere and invade webs only when full grown, or were they lurking in less conspicuous sites on the untidy trampolines?

The spiders, too, were most unenlightening. They hardly ever caught anything. One wondered how a community of several dozen spiders and bugs could subsist on such short rations. On the other hand everybody looked plump. Possibly they depended on prey that became entrapped at night. Bugs moved in the webs with deliberate footsteps, a leg at a time. Spiders hung motionless unless I happened to frighten them. Then they would suddenly engage in a wild circular dance, vibrating and rotating so fast that they became blurred. Upon ceasing this maneuver equally suddenly, they could be seen not to have changed their perches. Life in the webs came again to a standstill. . . .

Of course Tommy was delighted. I *did* collect a bug for him, for the thirty-seven remaining ought to be able to carry on as well as thirty-eight. Then, on a later date, I had to kick myself for having been so conservative. I found the webs greatly disrupted, and a pair of fat geckoes regarded me from latrine walls with their peculiarly blank eyes. Spiders and bugs had both been depleted to minimal numbers—I think I found no more than about six of each.

Should I declare war on geckoes? I decided against this. Possibly they would go away, now that prey was scarce, and the populations would have a chance to restore themselves. More important, though, was the reflection that Bush Bush Forest must be a natural habitat for these odd arthropods. When the latrine was built, they must have invaded it from nearby. Wouldn't it be even more revealing to learn where they normally reside?

Thus I began a search that soon brought new enlightenment. Under the eaves of We House; beneath the roof of an open shed where we stored scrap lumber, traps and other gear; behind old pieces of asbestos sheeting stacked against trees: in all these places I began to find tenanted webs of the same sort of spider, and in at least half of them were one or two bugs. These sites were still artifacts, shelters provided by man, but they gave me clues for proper places to look: the frail spider clinging to its weak snare must locate itself in protected situations, out of the wind and shielded somehow from pelting tropical downpours.

I ran first to a giant olivier near We House. I had admired the architecture of this tree since the first day I saw its buttressed trunk, supporting a soaring bole and spreading crown upheld by incredible, sinewy arms. When you look at such a wonderful structure and are captivated by its gross majesty, it does not occur to you to examine it with a hand lens. Hence I had never troubled to crawl in among the many buttresses to find what might hide in their recesses. The first thing I vaguely observed was a "whirring" spider, and when it calmed down there sat two indubitable bugs, as complacent as if they had been in the latrine. Several other recesses contained spiders and bugs, too, but I noted these were all on the westerly side of the tree, away from the prevailing east wind.

What other places might provide havens for these creatures? I found two more that could be called characteristic. One was within hollows of trees, either standing or fallen, but again in situations where driven rain could not easily penetrate to depths of rotted cavities or interiors of exposed root systems. The other sites were less secure but nevertheless frequently inhabited. These, as typically tropical as are buttressed tree trunks, do not figure in travel folders. When jungle trees die—especially if they are palms—termites, fungi and soil bacteria quickly get to work on the part of the trunk that was underground. Within a short time (a year or so?) a hole is all that remains. Ultimately these cylindrical depressions become filled, but temporarily they serve as spider and bug sanctuaries, as well as admirable booby traps for roving naturalists: I damn near broke a leg in them several times. The reason I dub them "less secure" for spiders and bugs is that they are exposed to direct downpours. On the other hand, they *are* protected from crosswinds, and I found them colonized often enough to include them among natural habitats of the spider-bug association.

Once or twice a year I used to go to New York, to attend scientific meetings or to confer with my peers at the Foundation office. On these occasions I accomplished everything in jig time in order to save a few minutes for the American Museum of Natural History before having to dash back to Trinidad. Such a trip was imminent, and I collected spiders and bugs without restraint. Arriving at the Museum, my pockets bulging with vials containing specimens preserved in alcohol, I inquired for the whereabouts of their authority on spiders and was directed to the office of Dr. Willis Gertsch. As matters turned out, his neighbor in that wing of the museum was Dr. Pedro Wygodzinsky, a student of creatures other than spiders that frequent spiderwebs. Dr. Gertsch called him in immediately, and the three of us had a great powwow. At last I could give the spiders a name: they were members of the family Pholcidae and could be called simply "pholcids." Dr. Gertsch said that this group of spiders is considered to be fairly primitive in the evolutionary scale. When I asked him how the bugs managed not to get stuck in the webs, he informed me that "almost all spiderwebs are dry— it is only the orb weavers and perhaps a few others that use the tanglefoot, sticky system." Cobwebs, therefore, are really more like bird nets, in which the trapping principle is based on Laocoönian confusion rather than viscid, tar-pit immobilization.

Dr. Wygodzinsky was equally revealing, but in his case it was because of what he could not say. "You are quite correct—nothing is known about the life history of these bugs. Anything you can learn and report will be brand new information."

On the return flight to Trinidad I conceived a new strategy. Life at We House was too brief and too filled with other occupations to give spiders and bugs their due. I must have them at my elbow in Port-of-Spain, within a miniature escape-proof container affording a constant source of food and with attractive places for all involved to pursue their sluggish lives. And where else but on the dining room table?

But first I must try a far simpler experiment. If the bugs would take to my tropicopolitan spiders in the study, I could forget about cages. Alas! the spiders took to the bugs. The first bug I released promptly got stuck in the sticky strands of an orb and was pounced upon. *Arachnicorus* is designed for life in dry webs.

I directed our carpenters to make a "hotel," with a "cellar" in which I could breed fruit flies; a narrow slot would lead to an upper chamber in which a few pholcid spiders and several bugs resided as guests of the house. Two glass sides would allow me to follow events.

All went well with construction of the box—the carpenters had long ago become accustomed to demands for outrageous fabrication, so they simply followed directions and turned out a perfect product. Food ultimately became the major problem, for I could never control its supply. Sometimes swarms of fruit flies and other game were veritable gluts in the dining room, while at other periods the downstairs kitchen went on strike and famine led to cannibalism among the customers.

To bridge eras of fruit-fly scarcity, I resorted to searches for grain pests in our feed room at the lab and also in some warehouses near the docks in Port-of-Spain. Mediterranean flour moths, Indian meal moths and drugstore beetles helped ease these situations, but they could be reared only slowly, and collecting expeditions for them were not always successful. I remembered that when Leon had his pigeons, the feed he bought for them was often infested with grain moths of some sort, so I asked him to buy some more at the same place. We put it in a coffee tin outdoors and I left it uncovered so that a wandering moth might find it to lay her eggs. "Dat wrong, Doctor," commented Leon, "motts come out de feed deyself." Patiently I outlined Pasteur's work on spontaneous generation to him, and he was amazed.

Although I had not discussed the matter with Dr. Gertsch, I reasoned that pholcid spider biology might be largely unknown, too, so I decided to try rearing some of these arachnids through several generations. In any case I knew nothing about it, and there were no books lying at hand to inform me. In the latrine I had sometimes seen female pholcids carrying egg cocoons in their jaws. These small sacs were woven tightly about the eggs, clinging to the contours of each one. Seen through the Optivisor, they resembled brown raspberries.

I was careful therefore to collect an egg-bearing female as well as three other spiders and half a dozen bugs. These were sufficient to populate the hotel without overcrowding it. Another reason for wanting an expectant female was that I had not yet seen any males in the webs. If I could rear a brood of young spiders, there must surely be some males among them. My experience with spiders had repeatedly conformed with the familiar observation that male spiders are midgets compared to their wives. Moreover, they could be recognized by their enlarged pedipalpi—bulbous appendages flanking the jaws that are used in transferring sperm packets to the females' genital orifice.

"A little knowledge," etc. Twenty-four spiderlings emerged from the cocoon. As with the tropicopolitan spider, this female removed herself from the brood and the babies hung in a loose cluster where she had formerly perched. They did not move for four days and then molted. After this they spread out and began feeding. At first their successive molts remained fairly well synchronized, but later they got out of step. Of course as they increased in size, some began to disappear, not mysteriously, since it was clear that the hotel could not accommodate two dozen adult spiders. But what I kept watching for was the divergence of the brood into two obviously different-size classes. Nothing of the sort occurred, and I began to entertain wild thoughts of the billion-to-one chance that the brood was composed of only one sex.

It so happened that I was soon to leave Trinidad. Dr. Gertsch had said that he would like "as many pholcids as you can get." While I had no intention of satisfying his request to that degree, I did make a rather thorough collection in the latrine and at We House and the adjoining shed on one of my last visits to Bush Bush. Having pickled them in a jar of alcohol, I donned the Optivisor in order to peer at their anatomies, when revelation came anew. The spiders were all about the same size, but approximately half of them were males! No doubt about it: some of them had swollen pedipalps and small abdomens, but the span of their legs was as great as that of females—indeed, slightly greater in some instances.

Now I remembered Dr. Gertsch's saying that pholcids were "rather primitive" spiders. I gather, then, that primordial spiders exhibited little sexual dimorphism and that it has been a more recent evolutionary development among "progressive" groups to hold the diminutive male as stylish. And back in Port-of-Spain I naturally was now able to observe what had been before my gaze all the time: the brood had grown up into males and females on a fifty-fifty basis. Not long thereafter I observed a pair copulating, if that term can be used for the strange manner of sperm transference in arachnids. Had I not known the secret of pholcid sexes, I would have recorded this as another case of cannibalism—attempted, at least— female by female.

But the bugs commanded most attention. Dr. Wygodzinsky had primed me with all sorts of questions. For example: Did bugs catch their own food or eat what the spiders caught? What was the basis on which the two societies coexisted? Where did bugs lay their eggs? And so on.

Eventually I found almost all the answers. To begin with, I once thought that perhaps bugs owed their immunity in the webs to being distasteful to pholcids. That hypothesis was dispelled during one of the outbreaks of famine: I saw a weakened bug attacked and eagerly sucked dry by a pholcid. This did not look like a last-ditch stand by any means, like shipwrecked persons on rafts at sea drinking their own urine, for I am taught that arthropods are so automatic in their reactions that even a starving pholcid would not eat prey that was taboo in its instinctive dietary. Certain caterpillars, for example, adapted to eating the foliage of carrots, will starve to death if offered only lettuce.

Conversely, I sometimes saw bugs feeding on the carcases of recently defunct spiders. Thus the question of unpalatability could be dismissed. Why, then, should pholcids tolerate bugs at all? I have concluded that this is because *Arachnicorus* walks so gently among the webs, as if "on the water," as I have suggested. Ordinary prey blunders its way in, creating earthquakes and general havoc. This signal—if not too violent—impels spiders toward game that may be small enough to overcome. Sometimes the bugs' promenades lead them almost under a pholcid's nose; the spider will then make a feint at the intruder, but the threat is only weak, presumably because the stimulus has not been violent enough. And, after all, the bugs do have wings and are able to use them. Yet I never saw one fly from potential attack. After the spider's mild sally, a bug would simply withdraw an inch or two, although almost breaking into a run.

As for food, the bugs didn't care where they got it. When the fruit flies were plentiful, every hotel tenant foraged for himself. Spiders had the advantage of being able to bind captives in silk, leading to subsequent leisurely meals. Bugs approached struggling flies cautiously. Frequently this gave victims a chance to escape. But when a fly had become mightily entangled, the bug could unfold its proboscis from the ventral position and extend it into easily pierced tissues. Again and again I suspected that the bug first injected some kind of venom, for the fly (or drugstore beetle or what not) would almost immediately cease struggling. I have no evidence for this belief, and it is equally possible that the bug's suction apparatus is so efficient that the prey was almost instantaneously desiccated. But other kinds of bug are notorious for their possession or endowment of irritating saliva (bedbugs, as I can fully attest) and to me it seems only a step from mere irritation to toxicity.

During lean times the bugs became scavengers, subsisting on spiders' "leftovers." At least they seemed to. I should think that spiders would do a pretty good job of exsanguination before abandoning shards of their prey, but the bugs always lurked close and moved in as soon as the spiders had finished. The relationship between the two organisms can therefore be defined as opportunistic, as far as bugs are concerned, and more or less neutral in the case of spiders. Nevertheless the bugs, though not parasites on spiders or even nuisances in the webs, are probably fully dependent for their survival on spiders' web-building. This is a curious biological arrangement that must have few parallels.

The answer to bugs' reproduction almost eluded me. Again I had the problem of distinguishing their sexes, and Tommy came over for a drink one afternoon to help me. "Males and females of most kinds of bug have differently shaped abdomens," he said. We looked through the hotel windows but could not discern any variation among the hemipteran guests. By this time I was sceptical about unisexual societies, but it seemed a good idea to examine lots of bugs through the Optivisor on my next visit to Bush Bush. This I did, straining my eyes in dark corners of the latrine and eventually collecting one bug, with a slight abdominal kink, that might be aberrant in the desired direction. At that, I had to stretch my imagination to consider it a variation on the general theme.

Only a few days later, before the newcomer could have influenced hotel affairs, Leon interrupted my lunch by asking, "What dat, Doctor?" He used sometimes to sit opposite me while I ate, discussing spiders and bugs, but he had the advantage of full-time observation when I could look only between forkfuls of whatever outlandish dish he had prepared. Besides, he had eyes younger than mine. Now he pointed to a tiny, black, antlike crawler in the webs. A baby bug! "Dere's anudder!" he soon exclaimed. "And anudder!" There were at least six, though he claimed to see tinier ones than I could, and perhaps eight or nine were present.

From that time on the information simply spilled into my notebooks. *Arachnicorus* lays red eggs, singly, either in the webs (against husks of old spider prey) or on the surfaces to which webs are attached. Young bugs are more nimble than their parents but have a hard time of it because they do not yet have wings and are therefore more dependent on "leftovers." They tend to remain near walls, out of sight (which is probably why I did not observe them in the latrine). I was not able to determine how many molts take place before they attain the winged, adult condition, but their growth is slow and must involve at least six stages.

What else did you ask, Dr. Wygodzinsky? Oh, yes, you said I should write a scientific paper about *Archnicorus*. Well, I am surfeited with scientific literature and prefer to record my information in this warmer medium, as naturalists used to do. Help yourself.

Chapter 13

VULTURES

*P*oint in any direction from We House and I'll tell you a Bush Bush adventure. South, eh? That makes it vultures.

Almost from the instant I reached Trinidad I had vultures on my mind, and I soon discovered that Wil Downs was similarly preoccupied. Our interest in this case was "honest" from TRVL's standpoint, for it was oriented to viruses. We knew that vultures were common birds—you could see them in the air most of the time, and they swarmed on the city dump. They were said to nest on the ground or in hollow trees in forests. Years ago James Thomas had shown Wil such a nest containing two half-grown fledglings that were covered with engorging mosquitoes.

What better virus sentinels could one find, provided that vultures retain neutralizing antibodies over long periods of time? Parent birds spend at least a month incubating their eggs: during this interval they must be constantly mosquito-bitten. Since vultures breed annually (at least I presume they do) and are long-lived, they get "booster shots" of virus from time to time. Fledglings, remaining in the nest for two months before learning to fly, ought to begin their careers with an adequate set of inoculations. Everything considered, vultures' sera should be libraries of recent and past viral activity throughout wooded areas of Trinidad.

Perhaps that information would be less helpful than what we

could glean by netting and repeatedly bleeding small passerine birds. But the idea was nevertheless challenging. And since our respective curiosities were bent the same way, Wil and I talked at several staff meetings about the feasibility of trapping large numbers of vultures.

Leslie Spence remained conspicuously silent on those occasions. After Wil had left Trinidad, I brought up the subject again one day. "No!" said the new Director. It transpired that vultures are held in high esteem by the local populace; an onslaught upon them by TRVL would give us an aura of unpopularity that we could not afford to court for a mere whim. Why should people like vultures? I still find the fact somewhat amazing, for practically all birds are beneficial to the public weal, if only the public took time to realize it; but perhaps because vultures are so large and so obvious in their natural activities, Trinidadians had become conscious that these birds helped rid the land of garbage and offensive animal carcasses. That saved trouble, and the helpers required no pay from government funds.

An article in the *Sunday Guardian* informed me that "corbeaux," as Trinidadians call Black Vultures, used to clutter streets in Port-of-Spain early in this century, mingling with unowned dogs to feast on garbage thrown from doorways. Popular sentiment was neutral or even against them then, and people often shot them, surely for no reason beyond their being living targets; no one would dream of eating them. That practice led to the corbeaux' withdrawal from the downtown section, and they have never returned, despite numbers of generations intervening during subsequent gun-free decades. But meanwhile an effective system of waste collection was instituted, resulting in less to eat in the streets than there used to be. Should a corbeau descend in the middle of Frederick Street today, it would first be regarded with wonder and then be run over.

The dump, at the northern edge of Caroni Swamp, is a marvelous spot. Every bad smell in the world is distilled there, to blend into a cumulative aroma that attracts every scavenger in the book. Rats, gulls, pigs, vultures, and—yes—human scum derive a living here from the offal of Port-of-Spain.

My thought was to erect a large enclosure, perhaps six feet high and twenty feet square, with a big hinged door at one end. The whole thing would be covered with chicken wire, and we would bait it with dead dogs or donkeys or any other carcasses that came to hand. The door would be propped up perhaps for weeks before we sprung the trap. Meanwhile we would provide new carcasses every day, until vultures overcame their suspicions of the structure and entered the enclosure as confidently as cardinals at a bird feeder when you put out new sunflower seeds.

Then, on *the* day, we would insert the final dead dog and wait until the trap was occupied by a struggling company of thirty or forty vultures. A pull on a long rope would drop the door and whap! the catch would be made. Now one would enter with leather gloves, needles, syringes, blood tubes, bird bands and the rest, not excluding clothespins clasping noses.

"Nyet!" said Leslie again. Could I guarantee that this would work? No. Was it possible that some birds might be killed, either when the door fell or during subsequent catching and bleeding activities? Yes. And consider the costs: with human scavengers abounding on the dump, we would have to employ watchmen to guard the trap day and night during the pre-baiting period, for two-by-four timbers and endless yards of chicken wire would look like gold to them, compared with castoff detritus of their usual commerce.

"O.K.," I said. "Let me look up something else that I read recently." In one of my scientific journals I located an article concerning the use of a narcotic chemical, Alpha-Chloralose, that had been employed to paralyze wild sea gulls temporarily. Mixed with ground hamburger and distributed in gulls' feeding areas, the drug had enabled investigators to sit comfortably at a distance until their arena was littered with sleeping birds. "What about mortality?" asked Leslie. Trouble was, some of the gulls had eaten more than one piece of bait and died. "Nein!" he reiterated.

Finally he agreed that I could organize a vulture project on one of the remote beaches of Trinidad, where the urban public would never see it. That compromise satisfied me, for I had often watched those birds gleaning the sands at Mayaro for fishermen's leavings of "trash" following a haul of their offshore nets. Indeed, a small whale, slightly alive, washed up at Nariva Point on one occasion, and for weeks after the local human population had steeped itself in meat, vultures tore at vestiges of ligaments between the huge vertebrae. Yes, it should be possible to bait and trap the birds in areas as remote as Leslie could direct. Even so, I could see that he still was not keen; and for many other reasons that enterprise never came off.

The vultures of Trinidad present several interesting aspects from the standpoint of pure ornithology. I shall come back to viruses, but meanwhile there are questions of both species and distribution. From the latter angle, it is a remarkable fact that vultures do not exist on Trinidad's sister island, Tobago. On clear days, a man standing at sea level can easily discern that neighbor. A soaring vulture over Trinidad, with immeasurably keener eyes, could not fail to be aware of it. But some birdlike response causes them to shun the terrain. People have actually attempted to introduce them there, for their worthy purposes, but they either died or flew away. One is led to wonder whether Trinidad's vultures are so sedentary that they do not travel across the Gulf of Paria to Venezuela, which is even closer. Banding studies could give the answer to that question, but these await a future worker not under Leslie's aegis. I am inclined to believe that the vultures of Trinidad move widely only in a vertical dimension. If they cross freely between here and South America, they should long ago have colonized Tobago without human assistance.

The Black Vulture is by all odds the most abundant member of its clan in Trinidad. Bold and clumsy, it appears prolifically wherever man pursues his untidy ways. Much less common and more shy is the South American representative of our familiar Turkey Vulture in the States. This longer-winged, more aerial bird may be seen singly, or in twos or threes, soaring over remote forests, either in lowlands or to upper heights of the Northern Range (I never saw one over Port-of-Spain, and Tommy did not have it on his "yard list" either). And here we come to the species problem.

A third kind of vulture, native to South America, is known as the Yellow-headed Vulture and has been listed as frequenting Trinidad.

This is where vernacular names may cause all sorts of conflicts in the literature. Unfortunately—or oddly, however you wish to regard it—the tropical representative of our *red-headed* Turkey Vulture has a naked *yellow* nape. Therefore one ornithologist after another, simply knowing the name "Yellow-headed Vulture" (which is not well y-clept either) continued to report the species on our island. I fell into the same trap and had some spirited correspondence about it with a doubting Eugene Eisenmann at the American Museum in New York. Finally in British Guiana, on our encephalitis expedition, I had the incredible luck to encounter all three vultures lined up on successive fence posts at the edge of a field: Black, Yellow-headed Turkey, and Yellow-headed itself. At last I could see the comparative differences. I wrote Gene an apology and scratched out the false passages in my Trinidad books. It is now up to collectors, not field buffs, to come up with a skinned and stuffed specimen before the true Yellow-headed Vulture can be accepted on the island list.

I don't mean to become lyrical about vultures, but it is a temptation. As long ago as 1929 I banded my first Black Vulture at a nest on the Virginia side of the Potomac River, north of Washington, D.C. At that time this was by far the most northerly nesting record of the species, though it has since extended its range. The nest had been discovered by my uncle, Harold Brooke Stabler, now ninety, on one of his excursions to headquarters of the Washington Biologists' Field Club on Plummer's Island in midstream of the Potomac. With my then not-so-venerable uncle and his late friend, Herbert S. Barber (now immortalized among entomologists for having discovered *Anopheles barberi*), we paddled across the river in a small boat to look at the nest and, hopefully, to capture a parent bird in order to band it.

Naturally we had no thoughts of Black Vultures. Uncle Harold had lived most of his life in that area and had never seen one. Nevertheless in his boyhood he had been an ardent naturalist and egg collector and was therefore familiar with the ways of Turkey Vultures. We sneaked up on the nest, which was among some large boulders. My uncle and Mr. Barber rattled sticks at one of the entrances, and I pounced on the departing bird as it emerged from another.

I brought out two downy babies, while my assistants held the struggling adult. "Funny thing," said Uncle Harold. "All the young buzzard fledglings I ever saw before were white." These were tawny. Now we looked at the parent more closely. All the adrenalin that had been flowing blinded us to the fact that we had in our hands a species that by current rules ought not be there.

That was a real "first" for all of us. My Bush Bush experience was therefore only a "second," in its way, though merely from my point of view. For reasons that will become apparent I must include a few dates in what follows.

On November 17, 1964, James Thomas discovered a Black Vulture's nest while clearing some of our established trails south of Moon's camp. Our men had orders to inform us of all nests, whatever kind they were, so when I arrived in the swamp next day, the first thing James did was to take me to the spot. It was in an extraordinary site, though at the same time quite usual. What struck me —"terrorized" is a better word—was that the two eggs lay on a pile of moldering "sawdust" five feet high within the base of a hollow yellow olivier that must fall at any moment. It was truly a gigantic tree, one of the largest oliviers I had seen. Not only did its tremendous weight rest on the thinnest of husks, its interior being entirely rotted away, but it leaned slightly from the vertical; I felt that I would blow it down if I so much as sneezed.

The parent bird had flown at our noisy approach and the tree still stood, so I ventured to clamber inside to look at the eggs. They were indeed handsome, larger than hens' eggs and marked with various broad blotches of dark pigment. The ground color was café au lait, not white as in eggs of the Turkey Vulture.

This was great luck. At once I began formulating all kinds of plans. We ought to be able to catch the parent birds with some sort of rig, and later it would be possible to bleed the fledglings at various stages of growth. Those babies would be particularly interesting, for at birth they might contain maternal antibodies to some viruses, transmitted through the egg, while later they should be subject to viral infections of their own.

There was no way of knowing how far incubation had progressed. This raised questions regarding trapping of the adults. If the eggs were only newly laid, manhandling the parents might cause them to desert the nest. Were we to wait until after hatching, when the critical brooding period was past, would the corbeaux not fly sooner as we drew near with some sort of bulky snare?

For that was the only thing I could think of: an ordinary bird net, doubled or tripled by folding it upon itself, and attached to two poles. If we could tiptoe up quietly enough, with one man holding each pole, it should be possible to get in front of the hollow's entrance and capture a bird as it flew out.

Moon and James agreed to that plan, and I proceeded to adapt an old bird net to the purpose. "Old" was an economical consideration, for nets are expensive and this one would be useless after a vulture had floundered in it.

But it was not yet time to act. Much underbrush grew in front of the tree, and more shrubs and fallen branches lay between the trunk and the trail that James had been clearing. In order to carry the net to its point of operation we must proceed in total silence, and the net must not become snagged on twigs. I therefore instructed Moon to clean the area facing the hollow, as well as a pathway from the trail—in gradual daily stints, so that the environment would not suddenly be altered to a degree that alarmed the birds.

He did not follow orders, but neither did the eggs hatch, so we were still reliant on my original strategy when I next returned on December 9. I then went with him and personally supervised the clearing operation, done in one session. "Next visit," I said, "we'll catch the corbeau."

December 17. We got everything ready at Moon's camp and rehearsed what to do. Moon and Motilal would be net bearers. I would follow close behind, carrying a pair of heavy leather gloves and a burlap sack. My job would be to fall on the bird in the net and then extricate it. We would then deliver it into the sack and carry it

to We House for bleeding and banding. Of course Leon and Mohan
—with his girl Toy—came along to observe the fun, but Moon
admonished them to lag far in the rear and not even to breathe.

I had never seen such a change come over Moon. He became a
veritable fox. His hunting instincts aroused, he moved without the
sussuration of a branchlet or leaf under his bulky, knee-high rubber
boots. At the last moment, he and Motilal began to charge to the
entrance, when the vulture flew out in an almost leisurely manner.

What in the world could have happened? Then we found what
a ludicrous act we had put on. The yellow olivier, though presenting a main entrance to its hollow, was riddled with smaller holes.
From where the incubating vulture sat, it had a perfect view, through
a small chink, of our faultlessly executed stealthy advance.

Moon said it was his oversight, and I insisted that it was mine,
but since talk doesn't catch birds, we set about patching up the
various peepholes with pieces of bark. At last I went inside and
sat in the nest: I couldn't see anything except the main entrance.
"Next week we try again," I pronounced.

Motilal, I had come to realize, was wise but unduly self-effacing
and apologetic, so when he mildly suggested later, "Why you don'
let Moon and James Thomas catch de bird?" I took him up on it.
December 23 was a day of deluge. While I sat nervously at We
House, Motilal took off to join the crew he had selected, and within
half an hour they all returned, Motilal carrying a sodden vulture
under his arm! They had discarded my triplicated bird net in favor
of a large, circular bat net, which, however, had not done the job
either. Instead Moon had struck the departing bird with the rim of
the net, knocking it to the ground. Then a chase on foot had ensued,
the vulture and its pursuers becoming more saturated as they dodged
under each bush. They ended up in wet entanglement about three
hundred feet from the tree.

I proceeded to do something most unscientific, i.e., I became so
emotionally aroused that my hands trembled and I botched the
blood-letting task. First I tried to locate the jugular vein on the right
side of the neck, but a combination of dark skin, thick subcutaneous

fat and an air-filled crop defeated me. Then I went for the veins coursing over the elbow joint of each wing, finally aspirating a meager specimen from one of them. Oh, well, that was only for virology. Meanwhile here was the bird for its own sake. At the least I could band it, and perhaps it had other lessons to teach.

The corbeau was strangely quiescent. In addition it was completely inoffensive. My nose had been practically buried in its feathers as I searched for veins at the short focal distance demanded by the Optivisor. Yet the only aroma I could detect was the musty one of wet feathers. I looked for mallophagans—feather lice—too, but could find none. Apparently this was a fastidious bird that paid full attention to its grooming.

Satisfied at last, I told James to let it go. "No, Doc," he objected. "It too wet to fly. I gong carry it back to de nest." That was about a quarter of a mile, admittedly a long walk even for a bird as large as a vulture. When James returned some time later, he told me a remarkable tale that I would have doubted from anyone else. He had set the corbeau down in front of the entrance, whereupon, despite its recent multiple ordeals, it had rushed up the incline and settled at once on its eggs.

December 24: Christmas Eve and all that. Although Leon and I were due to leave early on this day, I delayed our affairs long enough to have a further look at the nest. I reached the tree, but nothing happened. It was raining hard. Cautiously I began to enter the hollow, when the still-saturated bird barreled out past me, making great pedestrian speed into the undergrowth. I could see the band on its leg as it flopped past: good! I had not done the vulture in with my palsied jabbings.

"When what to my wondering eyes should appear" but a downy chick and an empty eggshell resting nearby! A Christmas Child indeed! In the season for rejoicing I gave thanks to the powers that had produced this baby thirty-seven days after James had found the nest. Thirty-seven days? That exceeded by a full week the incubation period usually stated for Black Vultures in my books. However I eventually located other records of prolonged hatching, and

I finally attributed this instance to the rains. If eggs are dependent on heat transfer from a sitting parent, and if the parent is sopping wet, shivering with cold, embryos will necessarily develop slowly.

Never mind: the egg had hatched, so who cared what its perilous embryology had been? Motilal reported that three days later the parent had dried out and was able to fly. He recognized it by the leg band: good again! We never detected a second parent at this nest, although my texts insist that both share in incubation and presumably they cooperate also in feeding their young.

On the last day of the year I found the other egg still unhatched. Shaking it next my ear, I heard loud splashings inside. Obviously it was addled. I "blew" it at We House, hugely nauseated during the process, and the shell is now a documented item in TRVL's museum.

"Junior" meanwhile had learned to sit up. Potbellied and covered with down, the chick looked like a child's woolly toy. The black beak and face contrasted sharply with a shapeless body that rested, tripod fashion, on the round tummy with a leg sticking out at each side. I tried to bleed it but could not get into the tiny neck vein. Wing tabs were so small that there was no hope in those appendages.

On January 7 I looked in again with more friendly motives. The horoscope that day must have ordained docility, for the parent bird flew only a short distance to a branch within gunshot range and the baby reclined passively, though regarding me with alertness. I was impressed by the fact that the hollow remained completely "sweet" from an olfactory standpoint. No need to postulate that these vultures were different from others: of course they lived on carrion of the most delectably offensive kind. But somehow they kept it to themselves. Well, naturally: if a stench advertised them to the forest, they would be set upon by predators before you could say *Coragyps atratus*.

Junior did not live up to his initial good manners. On January 13 he rose up at my approach and began to execute retching movements. Perhaps he had seen the needle in my shirt pocket, but in any case he let go for real as I handed him out to Motilal and then the retching was on my part. I obtained a very small specimen from the neck. Wing tabs were still much too tiny, though they were elongating, and I could see buds of primary and secondary flight feathers along their posterior margins.

One week later I returned without gory intent, but Junior had not forgotten. He had moved into a recess of the hollow, facing inwards, but now he backed out, turned around and lunged at me. I could almost swear that he cleared the ground, which would make it a jump. He had enlarged to the size of a small frying chicken but still retained the shape of a child's rotund toy, so that the maneuver of lunging—or jumping—was nothing short of ludicrous. Indeed at its termination he fell on his face. But it was an admirable expression of hostility, which I applauded. Not only that: he had hissed at the same time and had finally acquired an atrocious case of halitosis. "This will be a lordly vulture," I mused.

Viral affairs took me to Surinam for a couple of weeks, and it was not until February 4 that I could visit the nest again. Junior did not seem to have grown much, and his aggressiveness had disappeared. Was something wrong?

I'll never know the answer to that. On February 10, I clambered into the hollow and searched everywhere without finding a trace of the chick. For the first time I stood erect on the mound of rotting debris and looked upward into the towering cavity. Even now flakes of decay fell into my eyes, as organisms of destruction continued their unceasing internal attack on the huge bole. Some large bats, high above, shifted position and sent additional showers of detritus cascading down. I found myself a bit dizzy and grasped the nearest struts available: what were these but thongs of strangler figs that had already occupied the interior of their victim! But such sinews would never serve to brace the wreck—soon all would fall in a glorious communal crash.

Blinking, I emerged from the tree and saw what I ought to have noticed at first. The ground was strewn with large, succulent, sprouting pinfeathers that could have come only from the wings and tail of a baby vulture.

Possible culprits: opossum, snake, large lizard, dog, roving fishermen. What difference? I could write Uncle Harold only an incomplete report—and James Thomas must find another nest for TRVL. Who would have deemed the ancient tree more durable than the young life hatched in its womb?

Chapter 14

BEES

I cannot refrain from talking about bees next. Perhaps this topic does not seem a logical sequel to tales about vultures, but I never found beings in Bush Bush Forest to be sanely interrelated. Practically every organism, in fact, appeared to go its own way, as if the rest of the fauna and flora was incidental or absent. Obviously the cases differed, but I could not view any plant or animal that did not seem to prosper solitarily, as if it had been given carte blanche by some deity to fulfill a life apart.

Bird netting was often deplorably slack. Nevertheless I kept Motilal busy making endless rounds of the snares in practically all directions near We House and along the ramp extending across Petit Bush Bush Swamp. It was not that I was interested in getting the lab's money's worth by running his legs off: you simply did not know when a bird—or many birds—might fly in, and whenever that happened it became important to get them out in a hurry. If left unattended in the net, a bird might actually escape. Otherwise it would get more entangled with every passing minute, so that its removal became greatly complicated. Or the bird could injure or weaken itself, or it might be attacked by a predator. Obviously Motilal was not wasting his time, even when he reappeared periodically at We House to report one blank circuit of the nets after another.

Of course he did not really hurry. Sometimes, in truth, he would sit down to rest near one of the nets, so that that one at least received privileged attention in case anything happened. A few hundred yards west of We House I had a net in a particularly dense part of the forest, where Motilal found it pleasant to sit on a fallen tree trunk and enjoy the shade. And that is how we got into the bee business.

I say "we," but it was really Motilal's and Leon's enterprise, and I pushed my way into it only afterwards. I suppose they thought I would not be interested since we were, after all, working on birds. As I learned later, the whole thing began when Motilal was sitting on the trunk one day and noticed some bees entering and leaving through a small hole in an old branch lying on the ground. On his next run of the nets he picked up Leon and they trimmed off the ends of the branch with cutlasses, so that they could carry back the midsection, about two feet long and perhaps nine inches thick. This they deposited on the ground under the open shed alongside We House, where I happened to find it while looking at spiders.

Leon knew nothing, but he was Motilal's eager pupil. Motilal imparted a fair amount of verbiage, some of which turned out not to be true. I was so ignorant of details of apiculture that I could only listen and then try to sift facts from folklore. As I could piece things together at that early stage, these were stingless bees that nevertheless produced honey. The object of bringing them to We House was to "domesticate" the colony. Leon would get a wooden box in Port-of-Spain, large enough to accommodate the log containing the hive, and some time in the future they would harvest a liquid "crop."

But all sorts of questions bothered me, and I bothered my aides with them in turn. Stingless bees? Though familiar with that group, I did not know that they made honey. Motilal assured me that they did, immediately raising my doubts by stating that he had often gotten drunk on it. Nor did they look like other stingless bees I had seen: these were larger and in my eyes resembled ordinary honeybees. Yet my companions assured me that they had not been stung while hewing the fallen branch and carrying the section to camp.

And what about the design of the box? Why a box anyhow? Couldn't they get honey out of the log? Motilal said they "mus' bust de log" when it was placed in the box, to induce the bees to occupy this larger cavity and make much more honey. He seemed to know what to do, but I impressed on him and Leon that I wanted to be in on every future maneuver. Naturally they had to accept my intrusion. From then on I interfered in every possible way until at last they resigned themselves to the bees' having become my property.

At home in Port-of-Spain, Leon did a much better carpentering job, on a wooden box salvaged from a local store, than I would have predicted he could. That is not to suggest there were no gaps or uneven corners to be seen, but he somehow managed to transform a roughly cubical object into an oblong one exactly the size of the log.

The big argument then became "to bus' or not to bus'." We had all kinds of advice. Moon, James, various mosquito catchers—all came to We House to witness transfer of the sequestered hive into its new palace, and everyone had individual opinions that failed to jibe with other points of view. Finally I took a firm position: some-one had to. Better be conservative now. We could open the box several weeks hence and then "bus'" the sepulchre if the bees had not taken spontaneous advantage of their enlarged quarters.

My friends were not resentful of an interfering boss, for my co-operation resulted in placement of the box in a splendidly sheltered position that they would not have presumed to pre-empt. We secured it with nails and wire under an eave overhanging the "bedroom," and thenceforth if I could see bees at work while I lay on my cot at dawn, I had to criticize myself for oversleeping.

One observation was possible the week after installation of the box. Naturally Leon had made an entrance hole for the bees, though that was hardly necessary, considering that the structure was full of cracks and gaps. In the few days intervening between our visits, the insects had sealed every fissure with some sort of black material resembling hard tar and had even narrowed the intended hole (which they must have recognized for its purpose) to the diameter of a bee's head. I now remembered that the hole in the log also had been of that dimension. Formerly I had thought the bees clever to have found a home with exactly the right aperture: they were probably even cleverer in modifying an initially unsuitable one.

By this time bees were flying in and out in small numbers. It was impossible to guess how many there were, for I did not know the time each one foraged before returning. If I counted twenty entering individuals in half an hour, they might have been indeed twenty; or else ten, each making two trips; or five, each finishing four excursions.

Whatever the truth, the colony impressed me as a small one. The few hives of honeybees I had seen in the States always had so many workers coming and going that a one-way-traffic door would have been out of the question. We knew that we had lost a fraction of the community—perhaps a major portion of it. Motilal took me to the spot near the bird net where he and Leon had cut up the log, and at least a hundred bees were clustered where the hive used to be. They must have been honey gathering at the time of the rape, or possibly they flew out when cutlass blades began to fall. But then they were left behind, apparently without means of following a scent to the nest's new location or of recognizing their sterile sisters during forest encounters.

Then, when the log was transferred from under the shed to its perch on We House, another fragment of the population, out of doors at the time, persisted in clinging to the log's recent position only a few steps away. These may eventually have exercised a homing instinct, though I doubt it: some of them were still there the following week.

Thus we were in all likelihood starting out with minimal strength —all the more reason to be patient as honey reapers. Our chief asset was the presence of a queen. Had we lost her, the remaining workers would have given up their housekeeping devotion. Perhaps their zeal was actually increased by the greater burden now placed on the residual corps, for the box could not have been sealed with more speed. In addition a bee—or bees on a rotational basis—had been assigned to sentry duty. Plugging the entrance hole with its head, it surveyed each incoming worker, demanding credentials or a password or whatever sign they could exchange. Recognition was instantaneous, for the sentinel withdrew so fast that the worker hardly hesitated in barging home. Outgoing individuals probably prodded the sentry from the rear, when it also withdrew. In both cases, as soon as "friends" had passed, a guardian head at once popped back into the gateway, obviously on the lookout for foes. The to-and-fro activity of this responsible policeman must have been exhausting, which is why I imagine that they worked in shifts.

We were joyously enthusiastic about our early success. But through all this activity I kept worrying about what kind of bee they might represent. The combination of "stingless" and "honey" did not seem right. One day as Leon was sweeping leaves off the roof, he got stung in the eyelid while he was directly over the box. That did not sound "stingless" to me, and, as I have already mentioned, these insects looked like true honeybees. Tommy thought so, too, and when Dick Hayes, another entomologist, visited the swamp sometime later, he agreed.

The fact remained that during all the maneuvers—cutting up the log in the forest, transporting it, installing it in the box—no one had been molested, though bees filled the air. I could not make sense out of the contradiction between appearances and events, and the few books I was able to consult failed to resolve my questions.

Dick Hayes made one valuable suggestion. He was fascinated by what Motilal and Leon were doing but pointed out that we had omitted an important adjunct when we nailed the lid on the box. "You should have put in some comb frames, to encourage them to use the interior, or to accelerate their use of it." Good idea: I said we would make some frames out of laths and install them when we found courage to take our first look inside.

When to look? As time went on, the population seemed to increase, if one could judge by the frequency of arrivals and departures. Moon was the principal advocate of "bustin' de log" promptly, but still I hesitated. Then one morning before we got up Leon said, "Listen to de bees." I jumped out of bed and cupped my hands to my ears under the window. A droning hum emerged from the box.

Something new was surely going on. Perhaps the population had enlarged more than I thought and the old queen was about to abscond with part of her retinue, leaving the hive to several of her rival daughters. That would be worth witnessing, though it would leave us again with a depleted colony, and I could hardly believe that they had had enough time to reach a point of oversaturation, for the box was really spacious compared to the log.

I kept watching for an exodus all morning, but nothing happened. The humming died away an hour after it had begun. Possibly this was only a rehearsal of some forthcoming act. At any rate I could contain my curiosity no longer. "O.K., men," I said, "let's see what in hell is going on."

They were as impatient as I. Down came the box in a jiffy. But open it? Leon had purposely driven nails of the lid only halfway in, so that on future occasions they would be easy to extract. The lid was glued so fast that they had to pry it loose with screw driver and hammer. I read later that a somewhat similar kind of bee in the Orient is exploited for the substance it uses in sealing its hives: natives collect the material for calking their leaky boats.

To our chagrin the bees had not utilized their box at all. Although they had made it all but airtight, they had produced a huge additional amount of dense, black putty—which I then falsely presumed to be a salivary secretion—to fabricate a long tunnel from the original hole in the log to the box's exit. In effect the box might just as well not have been there, and the bees remained in the same confined cavity they had originally occupied.

Had the lath comb frames not been at hand, I would have consented to onslaughts that would expose inner secrets. However, a bit of quick reflection on Dick Hayes's remarks led me to suppress Leon's and Motilal's eagerness. "Maybe they didn't like the box because we failed to make it cozy enough," I said. "Let's put the frames in and give them another chance."

Somewhat reluctantly they complied, and up went the box again. During the half hour or so that their home was on the ground, I observed a repetition of the bees' inability to recognize slight changes of position of their front doors. The black head of a bolt on the wall of We House, just behind the box's proper location, now looked like an entrance hole to returning harvesters. Minute after minute more of them congregated there, flying in bang on and dropping, or else clinging insecurely to the asbestos sheeting alongside the metal bolt. At last I judged about a thousand milling bees to be present—many more than I had believed the log to contain or to be able to accommodate. "You know what?" I said. "I'll bet that humming had something to do with hatching a new brood. If that is true, now they'll *need* the whole box. So I think maybe we have put in the comb frames at just the right time."

Meanwhile no one had been stung. This was a ridiculous phenomenon, for our interference with the box presented the bees with far greater effrontery than Leon's sweeping the roof. Perhaps he had been stung by something else. Or possibly he had been violent in his sweeping, while we took down the box and replaced it oh so deliberately—except that we did have to blast it open with hammer blows. It was time now to settle the enigma: honeybee or stingless bee?

One astute suggestion had already been advanced by Dr. Jack Price, a Canadian biologist working temporarily at TRVL: "Maybe they bite." I hadn't thought of that. Now it occurred to me that Leon's eyelid had not swollen perceptibly. I made the new proposition to him and he rather wonderingly concurred. "Yes, Doctor," he said, "dat true, 'cause it don' make no bump like Jack Spaniard [a local name for wasp]."

A scientist can't proceed on mere hypothesis or hearsay evidence. On our next visit I caught three returning bees in a butterfly net and deliberately tried to make them sting *or* bite me. It is a rather uncomfortable experience to reach barehanded into a net to catch bees between thumb and forefinger; all instinct and prior learning warn you that you are being a fool. However, I did it, and then watched through the Optivisor as I attempted to make each bee injure me from either fore or aft. They struggled, but not a sign of a stinging apparatus appeared, even when I squeezed their abdomens, and the mandibles—though actively opening and closing—were too weak to pierce or even pinch my not especially tough skin.

So they were not honeybees, in the strict sense. By this time I was corresponding with Drs. Gertsch and Wygodzinsky at the American Museum in New York about spiders and bugs, and I had noticed on their letterhead that the Chairman and Associate Curator of Entomology was a hymenopterist, Dr. Jerome G. Rozen, Jr., precisely the friend I now needed.

I "sacrificed" the three bees—a scientific euphemism for slaughtering them to my own purposes—and sent them off to Dr. Rozen. Promptly he replied that they were "fairly close" relatives of honeybees, were indeed stingless, and could be called "meliponids." Instead of going further into the subject, he added electrifying news. Unbeknownst to me—so isolated can you be on an island even as small as Trinidad—a hymenopterist was practically a neighbor of TRVL. This was Dr. Frederick Bennett of the Commonwealth Institute of Biological Control. Fred, Dr. Rozen assured me, would be greatly interested in my bees and could answer all further questions.

So far not only so good but absolutely perfect! However, when I called Dr. Bennett on the phone, his wife told me that he was away on an extensive Caribbean expedition, investigating diseases of coconut plantations. That meant that Leon and I had to continue for the time being in our ignorance, and Motilal in his half knowledge.

As one might have predicted, the bees rapidly resealed their box after we had opened it. I assumed that things had returned to normal until several weeks later, when I noticed that workers were using two entrances—the original one in front and another, with a similarly small aperture, at the rear of one side. Both these escapes were now guarded by the heads of sentinels.

What better evidence could there be that the box was finally being used *in toto?* Fred Bennett or no, down it came again, and this time I was really due for a shocker. The same difficult opening procedure took place. I was no longer worried about stings and could pay uninhibited attention to another fact that I had learned from my books: the black cement material is not a salivary secretion but a mixture of wax and resinous or oily plant exudations. Wax was a further link with conventional honeybees.

When Motilal, Leon and I peered inside, we found that the tunnel

from the log to the front entrance had been restored. I had expected to see that. So far as comb frames were concerned, they could
not have been more completely neglected. But from another point
of the log a new and most peculiar tunnel had been built to the rear
aperture of the box. This irregular black structure was covered with
spherical cells the size of golf balls, paper thin in texture and each
provided with a small hole at the top.

As I exclaimed in amazement, Motilal resumed the dais. "'Dey
fill dose wit' honey," he said with no astonishment at all. I had to
accept his statement, for he insisted that all was in order; we were
not looking at some crazy modernistic experiment. But how, then,
were bee larvae fed? It would be fatal to drop eggs into such honeypots and hopeless to rear them in viscid swimming pools of that
Olympic caliber. Motilal assured me that a brood chamber existed
inside the log and that these external reservoirs functioned only as
storehouses for the colony. It was these globules that he was accustomed to gathering in the dry season. "But dey break very easy,"
he added. I could appreciate that possibility. Indeed I imagine that
a raid with cutlasses on hives of this sort must result in a gooey mess,
with only a small proportion of the globular cells salvaged intact.

I felt a bit guilty at having been so unrestrained by my curiosity,
for Fred Bennett should really have been on hand. That did not dim
my sense of triumph, however. In his absence, this had been all the
more a venture of discovery. And no harm had been done, so far as
I could determine. The patient bees sealed up the box a third time,
and two heads resumed their guardianship of the holes. Following
up a statement that I had read, I verified that sentinels are able to
sleep at night. Rather than plugging the entrances bodily through
dark vigils, they seal those apertures with tarry wax at nightfall
and open them each morning: my flashlight proved this true one
evening long after dark.

Fred Bennett, when I eventually got him on the phone, agreed that
we should wait until the dry season to do anything further. Yet this
was a turning point. Now the hive passed not only out of Motilal's
and Leon's domain but out of my hands as well, into the realms of
Science. Fred's designs had nothing to do with honey: as an apiarist,

he was interested in colonizing various types of wild bee. Furthermore he maintained a wide correspondence with similarly engaged scholars all over the place. At that very time he had received a frantic message from a Professor in São Paulo, Brazil, whose meliponid queen had just died, and that distant colony was pining away. Here was an obvious opportunity for all of us to do the good turn of a lifetime.

Fred relieved my mind by suggesting that we send the Professor only some brood cells, from which a new queen might emerge. Thus we—or rather he—could retain our own queen and thereby save ourselves from the professor's plight. Everything was finally arranged when Fred joined us for coffee at TRVL one morning and I met a handsome young entomologist who seemed well endowed with strength to "bust logs."

That he did with one blow of his cutlass. Wil Downs chanced to be visiting the lab, and of course you can't keep him out of Nariva Swamp, so he witnessed everything, having first been given a telescoped account of the bee saga. Poor Motilal and Leon took back seats without complaining, even as Fred told them how to lower the box and open it as if they had had no prior experience.

The interior looked much as it had before, except that now most of the honeypots were sealed. Of course Fred was not interested in these, so Motilal and Leon did get their rewards, though not before the rest of us had tasted some of the wares. It was a rather strange substance—a bit bitter and much more fluid than honey, in my experience. Besides, some of the globules, though looking identical to honeypots, contained an entirely different concoction—a sort of pollen mash with a yeasty flavor. Bread and wine for the colony: who could ask more?

Probably this hive would never have been able to exceed its present size, unless after years of use the bees had established brood cells as well as food depots in the box. The cavity of the log was pitifully small. In no time at all Fred found the queen, a feeble creature somewhat larger than the other bees, with a modestly swollen abdomen. Apart from that the log contained four or five tiers of waxy brood cells, each segment consisting of approximately a hundred sealed, honey-filled nurseries.

Log busting must be the end of the world to meliponids, I would have thought. But Fred knew his business. Of course the log had to go, as well as Leon's crude box. Instead, Fred had brought a hive of his own construction, neatly joined at the corners and provided with a perfectly bored hole. He scooped the queen and some of the brood combs into this, directing our men to wire the architectural gem into position under We House's protective eave. The rest of the combs went into a plastic kit to be sent to the Professor in São Paulo. Fred would return later to exercise further acts of hostility on our hive when the bees had recovered from the present disruption.

Throughout this exhibition, while Wil and I gawked, Fred had not only expeditiously transferred various hive fractions to their respective containers but also had quickly molded part of the black wax of the tunnels into calking material to diminish the size of the entrance hole of his own box, down to precisely a one-bee diameter. Yet he had impressed me as a relaxed, step-at-a-time individual. "There are all kinds of bee parasites and predators about," he said. "When a hive is open, they can get in and infest or devour it. That is why bees seal every crack and guard all entrances with their heads. It is a wonder you have been so lucky, opening and closing the box as often as you have."

I looked with increased respect at the wreckage of the log and Leon's citadel, now lying in shambles under the shed. As for the Professor, I don't know what happened, but neither did he realize how many foreign friends were wishing his colony well.

Chapter 15

SNAILS

*T*he first time Wil Downs took me to Bush Bush I was so shattered by the myriad things to see that I missed almost all of them. (As a matter of fact, on my final trip I was still making discoveries of plain-as-day objects that had been continuously presenting themselves.) Among my remaining initial impressions, as the boat snaked between buttressed trunks in the swamp forest that borders the island, were some strange green objects fastened to the spreading roots about a foot above water line. How these could have commanded lasting attention, when an entire tropical jungle was unfolding and the air was filled with squawking parrots, mystifies me.

Of course we could not stop—Wil wanted to present the entire show that day, and snail eggs were not on the virus stage. For that is what I later found the green objects to be. A species of huge fresh-water snail, up to four inches or more in height, is very common in many parts of the island lowlands. Local people—especially East Indians—make soups or stews out of them, though this creature is only distantly related to the edible European *escargot*. Trinidadians call them "konks," which is probably a corruption of "conch"—a marine mollusk having nothing to do with the case. Anyhow I learned that they belong to the genus *Ampullaria*, so that is the term I shall use when an official title is in order.

The masses were about an inch and a half long and half as wide —the size, roughly, of a full-grown caterpillar of the luna moth. And they were really beautiful—a light shade of pea green (again luna-like). When viewed closely (for I asked Moon to interrupt the next trip), they disclosed a marbled appearance which was the result of a whole mass of eggs having been plastered together. I never surprised a snail in the course of its oviposition and concluded that they must emerge at night for this function.

For some months I wondered why an aquatic organism should come ashore to lay its eggs. My first assumption—which was too facile—was simply that there must be underwater enemies to consume them. But shouldn't that work both ways? What about terrestrial threats? Eventually I worked out a more likely hypothesis. *Ampullaria* is adapted to living in the most stagnant of sumps. It may have some ability to absorb dissolved oxygen through its tissues—I don't know about that—but it is most assuredly an air breather as well. Among its various appendages is a long hollow siphon that it periodically extends to the surface to take in a new supply of pure atmosphere. Eggs, therefore, would probably suffocate if deposited in muddy depths.

During the dry season, when Nariva Swamp in some years dries out almost completely, *Ampullaria* estivates, burying itself deeply in the hardening muck and sealing its tender body within the shell behind a close-fitting operculum. Thus it can remain inactive for months, oxygen or no. At these arid times, when it was opportune to dig accumulations of silt and detritus out of the boat line, James Thomas' crew often exhumed sleeping *Ampullaria*, and we would see them scattered along the banks.

Once, after we had returned home, I found that Leon had collected one of the "pretty shells." Since it was covered with mud, he scrubbed it at the kitchen sink, dried it and finally placed the ornamental object on the dining room table. Now it shone with a dark mahogany finish, its spiral geometry exhibiting all the grace of a fine sculpture.

There it continued to lie for some weeks until I happened to drop casual mention of its being alive. "You joking, Doctor," said Leon.

I'm afraid I did joke with him, not only at times but often, and to him this sounded like one of my more transparent or farfetched efforts. "No, I'm serious," I insisted. "Let me show you."

We washed out a plastic cleaning bucket, filled it with fresh water and dropped the snail in. It sank to the bottom and lay like a stone. Leon looked at me sceptically.

"Just wait," I said. He went about some unimportant task such as cooking, while I occupied myself with higher things. Thirty minutes later I heard him call; he was gaping into the bucket as if a genie had erupted. There, in the depths, the giant mollusk had extruded an array of twisting appendages—"feelers," tentacles, or whatever they were—that now were sleepily exploring the plastic substrate as if to determine what foreign kind of swamp this might be. Then one of these arms bent upwards, elongated itself and broke the surface, opening its tip to disclose a breathing tube: a snorkel, if I ever saw one.

Snails such as this, and many terrestrial ones as well, effect security for their shut-in periods by secreting mucus that acts as insulating glue at margins where barriers against the environment must be laid. If the creature is endowed with an operculum—a shield attached to the fleshy foot that exactly fits the shell opening when the animal retires inside—mucus dries at the perimeter of this horny structure and prevents evaporation from the interior. Some land snails, not so handily equipped with built-in door plugs, cement themselves with dried mucus against whatever object they happen to be creeping upon when humidity takes a vacation. They can then be found on tree trunks, walls, stones and in similar situations, baking in the sun. No doubt some snails die, but locomotion is so slow in this tribe that no individual can run for shelter. Mucus is the only weapon they possess to combat dehydration.

On the other hand, mucus serves them also in fair weather (which means foul, from our standpoint). Fortunately their mucilage is water soluble. A trickle of rain, and doors fly open—just as I had demonstrated to Leon. Then, however, it becomes a matter of mucus and more mucus, for snails can travel only on roads of slime laid down by themselves. Their gliding "foot" is covered with microscopic, delicate, beating cilia which could never traverse so much as one grain of dry sand.

"Well, Leon?" I asked.

"Dat good, Doctor," he replied. "I keep him for pet." That struck me as an original idea—a pet snail in a plastic bucket—but why not? Naturally Leon didn't know what to do: he would have kept the beast in its unattended container until it confounded him by an exhibition of stinking death. As usual I was elected to the post of welfare worker.

Along the margins of the boat line I had seen some of the green egg masses on stalks of a coarse aroid—an emergent plant, *Montrichardia*, characteristic of riverbanks in the American tropics. Since many (though by no means all) snails are vegetarian, I took a gamble on *Montrichardia* leaves being palatable to *Ampullaria*. For the snail had soon extruded its entire huge body and was now coursing restlessly round and round its circular world on the prowl for nourishment. On our next trip we collected some *Montrichardia* leaves, as well as another shell, for Leon insisted that "dey mus' have company, an' maybe dey have babies."

Of course these snails are hermaphroditic, but it is doubtful that an individual can fertilize itself. Two snails, cross-inseminating each other, would indeed give us a splendid chance for babies, provided parents thrived in the bucket. I added a long, dead palm stem to the arrangement, hoping that some night one or both captives would scale it and oviposit.

Time dragged on but no eggs appeared. The snails ate inordinate numbers of *Montrichardia* leaves and seemed healthy. One of them must have climbed the palm stem one night, for I found it on the floor next morning. Perhaps it was only seeking escape, since it remained in the secure bucket thereafter.

You can't wait forever to learn—at least I am not that patient. After almost six months of this dawdling, I brought home a cluster of green eggs that had been conveniently laid on a small fallen branch protruding from the water at the edge of the boat line. We placed this in the bucket so that young snails could crawl down or, if they preferred, simply drop into the miniature pool.

Development was rapid in a molluscan sense. In a week the brilliant apple green had faded to a dirty gray, and a few days later Leon called me to see several dozen little snails gliding over *Montrichardia* leaves, the sides of the bucket and the backs of the oldsters. We now had a cleaning problem, for the infants were too delicate to handle. Therefore we decided not to clean until they were older. The environment became more and more foul as uneaten portions of leaves sank to the bottom and rotted, but I did not worry, remembering *Ampullaria's* adaptation to such situations.

Apparently I had overlooked one dangerous possibility, however. Some mollusks like meat as well as spinach. When finally it seemed safe to give everyone a bath, I could find only two or three surviving babies, and on the next occasion there was none. Then, whether through our loss of interest and care or a true decline in the snails' vigor, both adults died. Leon flushed out the shells and polished them, this time creating a dining-room-table centerpiece such as he had originally envisioned.

Nariva Swamp is almost entirely unpopulated by man, but the Caroni Marshes, southeast of Port-of-Spain, often swarm with our kind. This is where East Indians search for "konks." Their method is to wade barefooted into the muddiest places, especially where masses of water hyacinths have been raked into heaps at the sides of irrigation ditches. These half-submerged, fermenting mounds attract snails that can be detected when stepped on. The floundering hunters reach down for them, thereby becoming daubed all over. When I used to see bands of such filth-encrusted epicureans returning with great sacks full of snails, I wondered how *Ampullaria* could survive in that area. Yet tens of thousands of the creatures must have escaped. After babies emerge, the egg cases are visible as white objects consisting of chalky shells. On one occasion I visited the Caroni Marshes just after the main breeding season of snails was past, and the stems of marsh grasses were so abundantly laden with empty white eggshell remnants that the scene almost resembled a cotton field. Rather than becoming extinct, *Ampullaria* could cobble the mud of Caroni in a continuous stratum.

I have mentioned the possible existence of snail-egg enemies, aquatic or terrestrial. So far as adults are concerned, the case is far more clear, even after you get beyond East Indians and French chefs. Many sorts of wildlife, especially mammals and birds, prey on snails, despite the unpalatability that mucus might confer on such raw morsels. However, I learned of one predator in Trinidad that truly left me in wonder.

Returning from Bush Bush to the forty-six-mile post one day, I found Tommy and a visiting entomologist both sweeping butterfly nets industriously through tall grass flanking the boat line.

"This is Dr. Berg from Cornell," said Tommy.

"Nice to meet you," I replied. "What is your specialty?" (For it is almost impossible to be a *general* entomologist.)

"I guess I'm about as specialized as you can get," said Dr. Berg. "My field is a small and very obscure family of flies, Sciomyzidae, whose maggots can develop only on tissues of living snails or slugs. Most of them simply attack and eat what they need at the time, though a few species are approaching a more truly parasitic stage in which they invade the hosts' bodies for prolonged engorgement."

So Dr. Berg could make a living in this arcane pursuit? Most emphatically yes. Mosquitoes were regarded as entomological backwaters until it was discovered that they transmit a host of diseases. Then they rapidly became museum darlings. Today snails are recognized as vectors of the last major unconquered tropical scourge— schistosomiasis—a disease caused by blood flukes. Any enemy of snails automatically becomes our ally. Happily, schistosomiasis is no problem in Trinidad, but Dr. Berg's presence stemmed from a search for species of sciomyzid flies that could be colonized along with vast snail-filled aquaria, hordes of the insects ultimately to be released in areas where the disease is endemic. Their larvae should then reduce or eliminate the snail population: a pipe dream, perhaps. Yet it is this type of biological control that could save us from results of current practices with unselective chemicals that lead to indiscriminate tragedy for wildlife in general while effecting only partial amelioration of some hectic public health condition. Not that "biological control" is a total answer, either. With few exceptions all methods only reduce incidence of disease but fail to eradicate it. However, the biological attack, if a suitable one can be found, is like a laser beam—an avenue so direct and sophisticated that industrial chemists dissolve in tears.

I aligned myself temporarily with the molecular demons of Du Pont by purchasing packages of a most diabolical snail killer for use in my garden in Port-of-Spain. This was a concoction that contained not only tasteless poison but an entrancing lure as well, so that the marauding mollusks no longer gave thought to chewing through tender stems of seedling beans and okra as they had done formerly. But I gave up the inhumane fight at last, when a particular land snail became my best friend. I shall call it *Achatina*, though I believe it was only first cousin of that notorious genus (some of them have defoliated entire islands in the South Pacific).

A neighbor of Dries Jonkers uncovered two large eggs while removing compost to spread on flower beds. By "large" I mean that they were almost an inch long. One was broken by the spade, but the other he carried to Dries, who brought it to me, and I submitted it to Tommy. Everyone thought it must be the egg of a snake or, possibly, a lizard. The neighbor was worried because he had small children playing nearby in a sandbox. Since there had been two eggs, I postulated that they might even have belonged to a pair of Ruddy Ground Doves and been accidentally covered when garden trash was piled on their nest, unwisely built atop the compost heap. Dries suggested this to his neighbor but received the answer, "No, they were too deep for that."

When in doubt, do nothing and let Nature speak. Tommy turned the egg over to Raymond Manuel in the Entomology Section at the lab, and we forgot about it. Several weeks later Raymond asked me to look at something peculiar. He had placed the egg on some moist soil in a jar. Now the egg was no longer there—at least only the shell remained. Its entire interior had been consumed by a huge snail, huge in the sense that it occupied space where the egg had formerly lain. It still had pieces of eggshell sticking to its own exoskeleton.

After marveling at this phenomenon for some hours, we all de-

duced that this was not a predator but a baby snail, though we had
not dreamed that snail eggs could be so big. True, the *Achatina*-
like land snail in Port-of-Spain's gardens was a giant, but scarcely
as large as *Ampullaria*, which laid clusters of eggs that looked
reasonably proportioned alongside the parent.

Lightning does strike twice in the same place—sometimes. We
were still only speculating about the baby snail, for a small predator, initially unnoticed by Raymond, could conceivably have invaded the egg and grown to full size as it consumed the contents.
But many months later I unearthed a similar egg in my compost
heap. Thereupon I knew exactly what meticulous procedures were
required to find the truth.

As Raymond Manuel had done, I arranged a comfortable bed for
the egg on some moist soil and decaying vegetation, but this time
I sifted it all thoroughly to be certain that it contained no juvenile
predators. Satisfied at last, I put the material into a small plastic
box designed for keeping leftovers in the refrigerator. With its
tight-fitting lid, it made an admirably humidified incubator that
I could keep on the desk in my study and observe every day.
Even discounting periodic absences in Bush Bush, I would be
able to determine whether this Aladdin's lamp gave rise to snail
or other phantasmagoria.

When I found it, the egg must have been fresh, for it transmitted
a clear amber light as I held it against the sun. Its shell was thin
but hard—not leathery like reptiles' eggs—and was covered with
slight rugosities that gave it a texture of fine sandpaper. In shape
it was, as I have said, like a bird's egg, a perfect oval, whereas
snakes' eggs are likely to be more cylindrical and those of lizards
tend to resemble spheres.

The countdown on the episode was again tedious. It lasted even
longer than the corbeau's delayed naissance. I had found this gem
on July 18, and it did not begin its leisurely hatching process until
August 27. Then a week passed before the baby emerged fully.
But it was indeed a snail! To begin with it seemed happy enough
in its little box, burrowing into the compost I had provided.
A week later it clambered to the lid, and I released it on the cool

hollow-tile wall below our avocado tree. I hoped that my lethal chemical snail attractant had become vitiated or leached out by newly arrived rains that were now keeping the adjacent vegetable garden in flood almost daily. But how can you follow the course of a snail?

(Long afterward I reported my observations on Trinidadian snails to Dr. R. Tucker Abbott of the Academy of Natural Sciences of Philadelphia. My "konks," he said, were closely related to *Ampullaria*, as I had supposed, but should be called *Pomacea urceus*. But the garden snails were no kin to *Achatina* at all. The fact that he named them *Strophocheilus oblongus* may be enlightening to somebody, but it means nothing to me.)

Chapter 16

ONE COCORITE PALM

*W*hen our "yard" at We House was cleared in order to erect
the asbestos prefab, some saintly person decided to spare a cocorite
palm tree near the very center of that forest opening. Perhaps he
thought it would give shade. More likely, he decided it was not tall
enough to be a threat during storms and simply saved himself the
extra work of cutting it down. Whatever his reason, I commend it,
for the tree became a center of observations that absorbed much
of my time while I wasted a few pennies af TRVL's money.

As in the case of the avocado in Port-of-Spain, I personalized
this particular cocorite. I repeat that there is nothing more satisfying than to make friends with individual plants, oysters or fiddler
crabs. Hardly anyone knows this except old ladies tending feeble
pots of ivy, but they know it full well. *Viva* old ladies!

A cocorite—once you absorb the essence of its shape—can be
recognized as far away as a crow can be distinguished from a vulture, which is a good long distance. Its crown extends from the trunk
in a "feather duster" configuration, because dying leaves fall away
before drooping. Even at closer quarters, though not yet immediately at hand, one can already appreciate another cocorite characteristic: its long fronds carry leaflets in interrupted clusters, five or

six in a bunch, with intervals between, rather than in the regular spacing seen on most other palm leaves.

The trunk of this one had reached a height of about eight feet, above which the foliage splayed upward and outward in a fabulous fountain. Mature arching leaves were at least twice the length of the trunk—possibly even twenty feet or more. New leaves appeared at the center of the spray as vertical pointed spikes, triangular in cross-section, that ultimately began to feather out at their tips and proceeded to expand progressively down the midribs. Such growth was noticeably more rapid during the rains, coming almost to a halt in bone-dry periods. I could not guess how old the We House tree might have been, but during several years it seemed to remain the same height, despite production of several new leaves. It may well have stood there for one or two decades. In the forest close by I could see cocorites in all stages of development, from fountains springing directly at ground level with no trunks at all to lofty dusters atop boles not less than thirty feet high in their bare extent.

All cocorites except the youngest ones were colonized (if that is the proper term) by an attractive fern that grew in accumulations of humus in old leaf bases. Dead palm fronds never broke off cleanly from the trunk but cracked about a foot from their attachments. It might then take a year or so for these remnants to rot away. Meanwhile they served as perfect natural flower pots. Without ferns, this region of a cocorite would be the one unsightly part of its anatomy —perhaps that is why each one made certain to garland itself.

The fern was not particularly remarkable, its leaves being of ordinary shape—a single midrib with simple leaflets on either side. However, the fronds were long, some of them reaching two feet, and drooped gracefully as from a hanging basket. "Colonization" of a palm tree was obviously effected by wind-blown spores, but once a young fern established itself in the beginnings of a cocorite trunk, a lifelong association persisted. Ferns constantly put out exploratory runners as well as leaves. When a new "flower pot" appeared above, one of these shoots was certain to find it and set up satellite housekeeping. As old flower pots fell, a portion of the fern establishment might be torn away. Nevertheless, while a palm ascended toward the canopy, its own fern—the same one—went with it palm leaf by palm leaf.

Naturally flower pots can be contaminated by other wind-blown germs, as well as by seeds disseminated by birds. The cocorite in my yard usually sported several kinds of weed in its aerial fern garden. Among these I recognized various grasses, a "Spanish needle," and a thorny solanaceous plant, all of which grew commonly on the ground. Bad luck, I thought as I saw the puny show they made in those restricted habitats, for each leaf base contained only a handful of detritus. Yet determination is the all in all of Nature, and without exception those derelicts produced seed: not a rich crop—perhaps only a seed or two—but their individual tribes were none the less perpetuated, and Nature had *not* failed.

This tree afforded me satisfaction of a long-standing craving. Amid its adventitious companions was a young strangler fig that had not yet established connections with the ground, although it was about to accomplish that crucial act. I had always wanted to see what the response would be when the creeper or vine became transformed to a sapling. As a matter of fact, a sapling status was already apparent in the broadleafed stem that rose three feet from one of the clinging flower pots. But roots, coursing down the trunk, were the veriest of fragile filaments, lacking the diameter even of fern tendrils. Now the longest rootlet was about to strike soil.

I was curious about another aspect of the forthcoming event. The descending rootlets had deviated every which way as they encountered slight rugosities on the trunk. If they were to serve as future supports for a fig tree, the foundation would be a wobbly one. But fully established stranglers always seem to possess well-engineered vertical supports. How could this one straighten out its architectural confusion without dropping a whole new set of girders?

That problem would have been more formidable if my cocorite had been taller. Some failures result when stranglers germinate in hopeless situations such as outer reaches of horizontal branches in the canopy. However, in my palm tree the challenge must be minimal: I could not imagine a more optimal site for a strangler seed to have been deposited. Its roots did not have too far to go, and the host tree was sufficiently young to assure it many years of support.

Indeed, palms should be exceptionally fortunate fosters for figs. Their trunks do not expand appreciably as they grow older; whatever initial adjustments stranglers make with such supports are permanent and mutually acceptable ones. "Strangling," in fact, is not really a function of figs but the result of attempted increase in girth by ordinary forest trees. At least I think most of the blame lies there, though perhaps figs can exert some contractile force.

My reservation on this point is derived from what happened in the few months after the first rootlet buried itself at the base of the palm. Even after the first week I could see it beginning to swell. You might think this some kind of tactile response—it looked like one—but I am inclined to belive that the reaction was nutritional or, more specifically, a release from mineral deficiency. The natal flower pot contained only rotting organic material and such miniscule deposits of salts as could have been carried there by prevailing winds from the sea, more than a mile distant.

Whatever the true interpretation, this particular root not only expanded so rapidly that it quickly split its original thin integument but it began to shorten; where it had been curved, it straightened out. Soon segments of it, formerly hugging depressions in the trunk for dear life, stood out as rigid thongs. Other rootlets, not yet within weeks of landfall under the old regime, became suddenly invigorated and hurried down in a cascade. The sapling issued a new order of leaves. Everything betokened an infusion of vitality.

But what had this impoverished sand to offer other than minerals slightly in excess of those in leaf bracts? Tropical soils in humid regions are usually so leached out by annual rains that traces of soluble salts become the final bone of competition among populations of vegetation. Thus my strangler might be more of a threat to the cocorite than I had originally imagined. Rather than crushing its nonresisting host, it could do a greater disservice by exploiting the same root arena. If perchance figs are more efficient than palms in extracting minerals below ground, my pet "fountain" would decline. But I would need to spend years in Bush Bush to learn that sequel.

Not satisfied with the cocorite as Nature had endowed it, I added two embellishments. The first was a nest box for Tropical House Wrens. This was a structure that I had had made from scrap lumber a year previously, when I lived for a while in a shack at Mayaro Beach on the east coast. The box had been occupied by wrens there and consequently was already properly conditioned. I would not have thought house wrens adaptable to jungles unless they had given me the indication. A pair at Moon's camp once reared a young Shiny Cowbird, and as soon as We House was erected another pair adopted our clearing. They tried to make a nest under the roof's peak but were driven out by fumes from our kerosene refrigerator. I had begun a banding program and succeeded in ringing the two birds. Later one of them was found inside a Cook's tree boa that was captured by our mosquito crew. The other then went to bed every night under corrugated iron sheeting directly over my customary seat on the gallery. This one eventually recruited a new mate, so that a nest box became mandatory.

According to expectation, a brood was reared. The cocorite was conveniently at the exact distance of the closest focal point of my binoculars, enabling me to watch and wonder at everything the birds did. That was not enough for Tommy. One of his specialties is flies of the genus *Philornis*, whose maggots infest fledgling birds. "Why didn't you make the box with a hinged top?" he complained. "Then we could take the little ones out from time to time and examine them." But now the nails had rusted so firmly into the old boards that to open the structure would have wrecked it.

Three babies flew, innocent of entomological scrutiny. I waited for parents to make their next reproductive foray, wrens in the tropics nesting at almost any time. But now the box was pre-empted by wasps.

I noticed these invaders first on August 11. At the outset there were only a few, and they came and went in an irregular fashion as if the box held only a mild attraction for them. My guess was that they were gleaning something from the recently used nest, possibly spilled insect remains. But after a few days the wasps went to bed in the box and next morning there were suddenly hundreds of them swarming about, clinging to the side and top boards and passing in and out of the hole at a great rate. This could no longer be considered a scavenger hunt: apparently the first wasps had been scouts from a colony located elsewhere and, their report being favorable, a mass transfer to new quarters was taking place.

Mohan and Motilal suggested that I could get rid of them by waiting until they were all in the box that evening and sealing the hole (for this masterpiece was properly built without emergency exits). They assured me that these wasps were anything but stingless. I could easily believe that and did not consider a verifying experiment necessary. They were rather small insects, about the size of our familiar yellow jacket but with a slender waist. And they were yellow, too, with a few black markings.

Could my workers never learn my attitude toward Bush Bush wildlife? Get rid of the wasps? I was delighted to have them. No one could predict what they would do, but new information was bound to drip from their wings.

At our next visit no wasps could be seen. I suspected that some "helper" might have disposed of them for me, but everyone from Moon on down denied having interfered. On such occasions I often dispatched Leon to talk to them in the "boss's" absence, and sometimes he would return with a somewhat different tale. But this item still came up negatively on the lie detector.

I considered the episode closed. Wrens continued to sing around We House, but they showed no further interest in the box. Then on October 22, more than two months later, wasps reappeared, this time to stay. I suppose they were different ones, the first lot having turned away after their group inspection, but the second mission deciding that the premises were acceptable. Even so, the box must have been only marginally habitable. If these wasps normally nest in hollow trees, they probably are used to a cooler environment than this exposed structure would afford.

They now settled down to a type of domesticity that was quite slovenly compared with our bees. They posted sentries at the entrance hole, but these behaved more like a delinquent street-corner gang than conscientious guardians. Most of the time they chewed at the wood of the hole, not as if they intended to enlarge the aperture but just out of idleness. When other wasps wanted to enter or leave, they had to push their way through these insolent loiterers: I was shocked.

Despite the delay thus imposed on returning wasps, which gave me a good chance to look at them closely, I could never see that they brought anything home. However, they were just as diligent as bees in making repeated trips throughout the day and must have been harvesting something. Possibly they swallowed it and then regurgitated the material indoors.

By November 14 close to a thousand wasps were present. It was time to collect a few for Dr. Rozen. This I did with a butterfly net while James Thomas looked on apprehensively at a distance. "I know dat kind of wasp," he warned. "Dey 'jep-twos' and very fierce." I reminded him that I had stood directly under the entrance hole, studying them through the Optivisor, many times without being stung. "Den you lucky, Doctor," he answered. "Dey know you give dem good home."

Having chloroformed my specimens, I could examine them really closely for the first time. They had all died with their barbless stings fully extended. I don't know why they are called "jep-twos," but I could see where their "fierce" reputation came from.

Dr. Rozen was unable to give me much information except that the wasps belonged to a subfamily called Polybiinae and that they probably fed on caterpillars. Surely I would have seen them returning with even the smallest of caterpillars if they brought in their prey entire, so I remain convinced that they do their butchering afield and come back laden internally.

I was impelled to collect those specimens not only by inquisitiveness that could no longer be curbed but also because I thought I might be about to lose the colony. On that same morning a strange attack was launched by a column of termites that emerged from the forest, crossed the sandy yard in broad daylight, climbed the palm tree and went straight for the delicious wood of the wren box.

Ordinarily termites do not expose themselves in this fashion: I had seen a similar exhibition only once before, in South Africa, but in that instance the insects were collecting nothing more tasty than dried grass stems.

Leon and I were on the point of leaving, so I had to abandon the termites to their work and spent the next few uneasy days in contemplation of the battle that might erupt when the wasps realized that their fortress was only a gingerbread house. Perhaps they did realize it, for next week the box looked nearly normal, having been chewed only slightly on one corner. I never saw the termites again. Yet I find it incredible that wasps should have destroyed or even repelled them. Maybe the wood was not so yummy after all.

Through the rest of November and all of December wasps continued their busy activities at a constant population level, so far as I could tell. Then suddenly they were gone again. This time I felt sure that something significant must have happened and that an inspection of the interior would reveal one or more secrets. I waited until January 12, when for several visits neither a wasp nor a wren had shown up. The rusted nails had to be broken (which I had refused to allow for Tommy's maggots), but it was all worthwhile for the scene that now confronted me.

The box was full, from bottom to top. I use this archaeological order to trace the strata from ancient to recent. Two wren nests, one atop the other, were easily recognizable: they occupied the lower third of the cavity. Remaining space was utilized completely by eight tiers of paperlike combs in which wasps had reared a new generation. These combs were 11 centimeters in diameter and punctuated by beautifully hexagonal cells each 3.3 millimeters across, as neatly laid out as tiles on a bathroom floor. A bit of arithmetic and geometry led me to the belief that wasps reared about 6,800 babies in this sanctuary. "A good home," as James Thomas said.

My other adornment of the cocorite palm was an orchid plant. I found this on a fallen branch in the forest one day and tied it to the trunk, just under the wren box, with a piece of string. That was a most inexpert thing to do, and I had no real expectation of reaping corsages from the act. In truth, I simply felt uneasy to see an orchid plant lying on the forest floor, where it would surely die. Tommy knows all about orchids, of course, and when he saw what I had done he immediately said that this was a very unfavorable place—too exposed. Well, a tree was better than the ground, and I decided to leave my derelict on the cocorite because there I could observe it more easily than in the sheltered spot at once recommended by Tommy.

Even experts are wrong at times. I take no credit whatsoever for the way that plant thrived, nor can Tommy be discredited: it simply flourished in a zone lying between my ignorance and his idealism. Almost at once it began putting out clinging roots that within a year's time circumnavigated the trunk. The original piece of string rotted away, but a procession of more and more roots eventually secured the plant more firmly than string had ever done. At first the orchid consisted of two small pseudobulbs, fleshy stems bearing a few short, broad, thick leaves. In its new situation, so unexpectedly acceptable, it quickly began to generate a new shoot, from the root base, that developed into a more luxuriant pseudobulb. And a year later it put out another even larger one, which soon terminated not in a leaf but a flower spike.

Tommy had at once identified the orchid as a white virgin, *Caularthron bicornutum.* That led me to do a bit of reading, and I came up against two provocative statements. The first said that blossoms of this species are sometimes "cleistogamous," which means that they do not open. Such an anticlimax would be terrible! The second note explained the "virginal" appelation as deriving "from the striking resemblance to be seen at the center of the flower." If this one were cleistogamous, how could one ever see the striking resemblance? And what was the resemblance anyhow?

Thus whetted by anxiety, I became greatly vexed to discover that I was not the only one interested in that floral spike. Soon after it appeared, I found a large ant at its apex. Instead of knocking it off at once, I looked to see what it was doing and could detect no activity: it just reposed there. Obviously this was not one of my leaf-chopping Port-of-Spain bachacs, but it made me uneasy, so I broke my sacred rule and flicked it away. Half an hour later it was back. This time I was even more profane and made sure to step on it. Another half hour, and a second ant was at the same station. After killing five or six single ants in succession, I realized that a new lesson was trying to claim my mind. Orchids are splendid, but so are ants: then let's see what this is all about. The stalk, I can assure you, kept growing with no sign of injury. Within two months, always with an ant in attendance, it became a foot long and flared out at its tip into five distinct blossom buds.

I had noticed one slightly ominous effect of the impassive ants. Whenever I removed one, a tiny drop of sap exuded from the place where its mouth had been. So they were not chopping but merely drinking. I suppose that was deleterious to some extent, but no scars were produced and the swollen pseudobulbs looked fat enough to supply spare moisture to solitary ants without depleting themselves.

Happily I was soon to go to New York for a conference and would be able to take time out for a quick trip to Swarthmore. There I could confer with Dr. Neal Weber, of the college's biology department, one of the greatest ant experts of our day. Neal was the last graduate student of that late famed myrmecologist, William Morton Wheeler of Harvard, who put ants on the map for all time.

I collected a few specimens at intervals, one ant always obligingly taking its station on the bud after a predecessor had been removed. Neal looked at the alcoholically preserved carcasses under a binocular dissecting microscope while I eagerly inquired whether he could tell me anything about them. "I can do much better than that," he said. "I'll give you a copy of an article I wrote on the subject."

Thank goodness for such people! On the returning plane to Trinidad, I read that my ants belonged to the "ponerine" division of that great branch of Hymenoptera and were named *Ectatomma ruidum*. Not that the exact Latin name mattered; I could now call them simply ponerine ants. But Neal's account of their biology told me what they were doing on the white virgin, as well as other forms of behavior I had not observed. The reason he had written about them at all is that they are predatory as well as sap suckers. Sixty years ago they were proposed for importation to the United States because in Guatemala, where they are known to indigenous Indians as "keleps," they apparently kept cotton crops free of boll weevils. In addition these ponerines have been observed to kill caterpillars and to rob leaf-cutting ants of bits of papaya blossoms and fruit, though generally they seem to feed, as Neal wrote, at "extra-floral nectaries."

I guess my bud should be called a *pre*-floral nectary, but the quibble seems superfluous. As long as it was a nectary at all, ponerines would respect and spare it. Now I could forget about ants and concentrate on orchids. And it was high time to emphasize botany, for swelling balloons were at a point that would soon disclose whether or not they remained cleistogamous.

They didn't! While friendly wasps buzzed about, I stood on a chair and looked through my Optivisor at the interiors of two opened blossoms three days before the immaculate birth. There, at last, stood the "striking resemblance." Petals of the blooms were white enough to justify fancies of virginity, but the complicated apparatus within was fashioned far more convincingly like a robed angel with spreading arms, as one might see above a church altar. I hope to be excused for mentioning that the angel possessed yellow cheeks that were actually masses of pollen. Things were rigged in such a way that insects, entering to gather honey in deeper parts of the flower, must kiss the virgin's face before descending between her outstretched arms. A blessing upon reproduction!

I worried (without appreciable anguish) about ponerine ants, for they disappeared as soon as the orchid unfolded. This small plant could not sustain them the year round anyhow. Then one day I discovered scores of them feasting on sticky blossoms of *Heliconia* all about the We House clearing. Here they maintained the same stolid immobility, although a dozen or more might crowd on one flower head. The white virgin apparently could not support more than one at a time, and ants somehow adjusted to its meager potential for yielding sap.

Tommy was naturally impressed by events that had gone against his prognosis, but he was also receptive to the rest of my hobbies,

more than I had realized. One day he brought a group of visitors to Bush Bush to demonstrate our multiple activities regarding viruses. When they had completed the morning tour, everyone came to We House for lunch and Tommy entertained them with a nonviral round of the yard.

"Brooke knows every single thing that's going on in this small area," he said. "Here you can see a bracket fungus that he's been watching for months. And this one palm tree—why, it's a veritable museum! You see the exploring roots of this strangler fig? The wasps in that wren box? That orchid plant? These abandoned nests of trap-door spiders halfway up the trunk?"

Trapdoor spiders! I couldn't let Tommy down at that point, but I had thought the objects were empty cocoons of some kind of moth. Trapdoor spiders ought to be in the ground, or so I had believed. "Yes, indeed," I said meekly.

I wonder what else I missed on the cocorite palm.

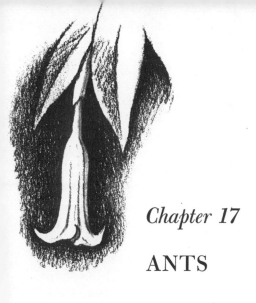

Chapter 17

ANTS

*I*f ponerine ants are no more than unimportant curiosities in Trinidad, some of their distant cousins go to opposite extremes in seriously affecting the island's economy, while others are at least obtrusive enough to be termed annoying. Army ants could be placed in the latter category, since they generally confine themselves to forests and shaded cocoa plantations where only the rural fraction of the human population encounters their legions. As a rule it is easy to avoid them, for the black columns are conspicuous even in those crepuscular areas. Perhaps I consider them more apparent than they really are, having learned by experience that it is always good policy to be on the alert. One does not look forever into the canopy for birds but at every step or two one glances at the ground directly ahead for processions on their restless marches.

Of course at night the matter becomes more complicated. Army ants are supposed to go to sleep after dark, but they don't always do so at once. Elisha Tikasingh will remember the time we left We House after supper to check some mammal traps for early entries. As I examined one trap by the light of a head lamp, Elisha unknowingly stood alongside at the very center of a traveling horde. Suddenly I heard him yell, and by the time we had left that place at incredible speed and completed "de-anting" him, he had learned the lesson indelibly, too.

Not all Trinidadians are familiar with army ants. By way of contrast, every last soul on the island knows what a bachac is. I have referred to my battles with bachacs in the Port-of-Spain garden. The same struggle was going on all over the island. In Latin America these ants have popular names (not "bachac"), the terminology varying from place to place. Brazilians, for example, call them "sauvas," and a classical couplet says, in translation from Portuguese, "Either Brazil kills the sauva, or the sauva kills Brazil." Even scientists have a variety of common names for them: leaf-cutting ant, parasol ant, or fungus-growing ant, whatever your choice.

Gardening columns in the local newspaper often featured the maraudings of Trinidad's bachacs, invariably including a statement that I must insist is utterly false. Again and again the public was told that these insects work only at night and that one must go out with a flashlight after dark to trace the leaf-bearing columns to their burrows. The picture presented was that of a lovely garden at sundown and a stripped stand of stalks next morning, with no sign of the destroyers. Also it was stated that unless you followed living ants to their burrows, you would never find entrances to the subterranean fungus gardens.

I am willing to grant that at certain times bachacs are more active at night than during the day, but this has nothing to do with their being nocturnal. After a bit of leaf or blossom has been snipped from a plant, it must be hurried to the nest before it wilts. At noon on a hot day in the dry season, desiccation takes place rapidly. Ants then either give up their labors for the time being, or else they continue their efforts in a blind sort of way, dropping a burden if it dries out on the homeward trail. But if the day is cloudy or rainy, bachacs forage without interruption.

As for finding their burrows, this is ridiculously easy. I agree that following living ants is the handiest method, but there is little need for flashlights, unless you want to make a spectacle of yourself by using one at midday. However there are two additional guides. One is the trail of dropped cuttings that usually lines bachacs' pathways, and the other is the path itself. I doubt that it is a myriad of ant footfalls that beats down such courses: the insects must do a bit of intentional clearing to establish them. Thereafter they stick to those runways, maintaining them in a semi-tidy condition, and one can follow a track of this sort across a lawn as simply as reading a road map.

In some situations gaps occur. Sidewalks, for example, bring one to a halt, for bachacs do not always cross this kind of barrier directly. Like the fox that wades downstream before emerging on the opposite bank, ants may confuse the hunt by taking advantage of a clean promenade. The quarry is not attempting to be evasive. Its nest is a permanent one, and bachacs are bound to return to it. The chief defensive ruse they employ—unwittingly, of course—is to locate nests where they are hard to get at. What one wants to do (if one is not a devoted entomologist) is to pour some kind of poisonous chemical solution down the burrow, but that requires an entrance hole accessible to the spout of a teakettle. Presumably bachacs have enemies other than that newcomer, man, and during the aeons of their evolution they have acquired an instinct to construct nests in the nastiest of quarters, in twisting roots or obdurate rubble.

I must confess to repeated operation of the teakettle in my garden —and in neighbors' gardens when I traced defoliating bachacs to their premises. How craven can you get? My motivation was based on an insane fondness for okra, of which bachacs are equally insanely fond. Had I been content to confine myself to cucumbers and Kentucky Wonder string beans, which leaf cutters won't touch, I could have avoided all this strife. And then I could have served Neal Weber, far away in Swarthmore, honestly.

As it was, I wore a continuous halo of guilt. Neal particularly needed a bachac colony for his current research into the suspected ability of these ants to elaborate and secrete antibiotic substances. He explained to me that the funguses they grow on moldering leaves below ground (such fungi—not the leaves—being their sole diet) are raised in "pure culture," that is, they are never contaminated by other funguses or by bacteria that must be tracked in on the feet of each returning ant. Somehow the insects are able to maintain cleanliness in the absence of doormats. How else could this be done but by chemical means?

In my usual cooperative vein, I promised Neal to keep watch for a nest that could be excavated conveniently. He wanted a queen, some workers, and a sample of the fungus as minimum beginning stock for his investigation. In his air-conditioned lab at Swarthmore he had a neat setup of plastic boxes and tubes, designed to please both himself and the ants. By special arrangement with a local florist he could obtain faded rose petals even in winter to feed them. The U.S. Bureau of Entomology and Plant Quarantine issued a permit for me to ship bachacs from Trinidad, and Neal gave me exhaustive instructions for packing them. Yet here was I with my okras and my teakettle, ruining my self-esteem both in the garden and at the dining table.

Neal got me out of that moral mess by coming to Trinidad one summer. He was an old hand on the island, having worked with Dr. William Beebe long ago, and had set foot in Nariva Swamp years before I ever heard of that paradise. On the present occasion he brought some Swarthmore students along, to give them a glimpse of tropical biology, but his main purpose was to collaborate with the Agricultural College on entomological problems. Naturally he kept his personal interests in mind, too. A Bush Bush trip to collect bachacs was a logical proposal for us both to make and embrace, so long as we blinded ourselves to the more logical expedient of collecting them directly on Agricultural College grounds in nearby St. Augustin, where they not only abounded but would be easier to dig out. But hell, that wouldn't be much fun.

We worked out (with some mental squirming, I'll admit) partial justification for the hardier venture. The rainy season had set in, and Neal said that by this time most bachac nests would have fulfilled the annual reproductive cycle that culminates in departure of daughter queens. New colonies would still be so small that we might not find any, and old established ones would be so vast that we might have to dig endlessly to locate an ancient queen.

Had I, he wondered, by any chance noticed anything in Bush Bush Forest resembling a fairly recently established colony?

"Fairly recently" was a tough question. I *had* seen one, south of Moon's camp on the way to the corbeau's nest, but it had not occurred to me to write down dates, and I really couldn't say when I had first become aware of it. Besides, it might by that time have already been well advanced in its development. I gathered from Neal that bachacs all over Trinidad are of the same species, but their prosperity varies according to the terrain. Thus the ones that fell before my teakettle in Port-of-Spain were actually almost below the threshhold strength of Neal's purposes (so I said to myself): perhaps not more than a hundred ants composed an entire society, and the burrow was a simple hole in the ground as wide as your thumb.

Bush Bush provided these gleaners with opportunities to "explode" without detectable limits to expansion. Any nest, surrounded by scores of towering forest trees, was within reach of limitless food, or, I should say, sources of compost for fungi. However, a large enterprise imposed engineering consequences on these domiciles that ants living in smaller colonies could ignore. Ventilation became a critical concern, whether for aeration of fungus gardens or simply to eliminate metabolic heat from thousands of gardeners and larvae.

Whatever the answer, Bush Bush nests bore no resemblance whatsoever to those in my Port-of-Spain yard or on lawns of the Agricultural College. Here, in the abyss below canopy branches, bachacs throw up great mounds of sandy soil, sometimes two feet in depth. Instead of trimming tiny grass trails on the bowling green, they denude every overhanging shrub and sapling to heights taller than a man and then establish foot-wide radiating roadways into the surrounding jungle. Some of the cleared arenas thus literally chewed into existence measure as much as a hundred feet in diameter, creating forest openings that endure for years after nests become inactive. For some reason seedlings do not reclaim such gashes as quickly as they repair rents caused by falling trees. We almost built We House on an abandoned site of this sort because it looked so inviting. Luckily James Thomas recognized its origin and warned us that foundations would never remain stable as decay progressed below.

A thriving colony of this size is by no means populated throughout its extent. Apparently fungus gardens are used on a rotational basis, and some worn-out beds may be abandoned permanently. This is what Neal was referring to when he mentioned the difficulty of unearthing a queen from so vast a field. However, some clues to active regions are always present. Returning ants, laden with fresh leaf fragments, surely are not interested in obsolete back doors. Ventilating shafts, likewise, will not be kept in repair where they are no longer needed. Hence it is the prudence of a bit of patient watching that pays off, rather than indiscriminate inroads of the shovel.

The nest below Moon's camp had really only one thing to recommend it: it was *not* one hundred feet in diameter. I told Neal that it might measure no more than ten, though I was not sure. My description satisfied him, and one morning we arrived, students and all, for the ceremony. Naturally we enlisted Moon and members of his tribe in the proceedings, every one of whom was delighted by such an occult diversion. In addition, Dries Jonkers happened to be on hand for one of his equally esoteric mushroom sorties.

Neal's first reaction was pessimistic. The nest, he said, was larger than he would have suspected from my account. I was rather astonished, too, for it measured more like thirty feet across than ten; it must have grown rapidly since I had last seen it. Crowded ant columns were arriving from several directions and disappearing into a number of widely separated entrances. It would be difficult to locate the nest's center, and we might turn up nothing but workers. Indeed Neal could have scooped that caste from the ground, if that was all he wanted, and would have obtained more than one kind, for I saw some small ones hitchhiking on petals carried by a larger sort.

But talking didn't excavate anything. Moon wore knee-high rubber boots, up which ants could not crawl, making him the logical one to dig. For some incomprehensible reason Neal was shod only in sneakers, but he was determined to dig also. He tucked his khakis into the tops of his socks, and the spades began to ply.

Bachac nests in some parts of the American tropics are extremely deep; I have seen photographs of myrmecologists' activities that looked as if a bulldozer had been at work. We were pleasantly astounded when the first few turns of the spades brought a boiling mass of ants to the surface. In retrospect I realize that this should have been expected, for Bush Bush "Island" is only a few feet above the surrounding swamp level and a shallow water table would restrict bachacs' workings to a superficial stratum.

Strapping ants with great hooked mandibles rushed to the attack. While Moon remained immune, Neal's sneakers and socks were covered in a twinkling with warriors that simply sank their jaws into the fabric and held on. As he leaned down to remove some of them, he was bitten on the thumb. This ant also refused to let go, and Neal had to dismember it before he could extract the fangs. His wound bled profusely; soon all his plastic boxes and other gear were daubed with gore.

He was ecstatic. He had discarded his shovel and was telling Moon where to dig. Almost every turn brought something valuable to light. Chunks of the fungus garden, resembling a sort of black cheese riddled with holes, were a delight that compensated for agonies inflicted by other ants that had now gotten inside Neal's clothing. He worked like fury, of course, to bring torture to the earliest possible end, but prizes had to be collected first. Some large winged females were particularly welcome discoveries at one point of the nest. Neal said it was late in the season for them, but that their presence indicated that the colony had not yet undergone its reproductive dispersal. Everything was in readiness for an exodus, but we had arrived just in time.

Thus the colony might be fairly young after all. Neal asked Moon when he had first noticed it, and his estimate was roughly the same as mine—not precise, but in agreement as to being recent rather than a year ago.

They did not find a queen, but this did not seem to diminish

Neal's satisfaction. All his bloody boxes were filled with various specimens—fungus, workers, soldiers, young females and perhaps other items: all alive, of course, so that they could continue their destinies in his air-conditioned lab in Swarthmore. Lack of a queen would not hamper his research, for Neal said that the unmated young females would nevertheless lay eggs in his cages and the workers would tend them and their ensuing larvae. According to rules of the most progressive hymenoptera of which bachacs are haughty representatives, unfertilized eggs would all develop into males. Sons would be unable to impregnate their mothers, since that act must be performed in flight, so the colony in the lab would eventually become extinct. But that would take a long time: Neal had enough stock on hand to keep him busy for ages.

The rest of us had been standing around, marveling at Neal's fortitude, because ants rapidly spread in all directions and were giving us trouble, too. But while we contended with single ones, he was ignoring twenty. We now got him some distance away and systematically de-anted him. Not all the blood had come from his thumb.

That might sound like enough punishment for one myrmecologist on one day, but don't underestimate Neal's enthusiasm when it comes to ants. I have already mentioned army ants as nuisances to be avoided: Neal's idea is to wade right into them.

After lunch at We House, having accomplished the bachac mission, Neal set his students to work collecting as many kinds of ant as they could find, telling them also to make notes on what each species seemed to be doing—whether it was on the ground, in a tree, etc. Not far beyond the latrine we found a narrow column of army ants crossing the trail. This provided a much better lesson in ecology, for the students had soon complained that the ants they located weren't doing anything. These restless creatures, on the contrary, were hurrying along a two-way traffic highway, those traveling west carrying captured prey in their jaws. Neal called his tyros from other pursuits to concentrate on the army. They were given forceps and small jars of alcohol. Each laden ant was to be snatched from the column and dropped into preservative. Later at Swarthmore the nascent biologists could identify assortments of caterpillars, grasshopper legs and so forth, to compile an analysis of the dietary of such predators.

Moon, Dries and I listened while Neal continued to lecture, though not for our benefit. He said that somewhere there must be a bivouac to which the workers were returning with their slaughtered meat. These ants are nomads and move their bivouac every day. And that is quite a maneuver, for it means transporting the entire dependent population—queen, eggs, larvae, pupae and the caste devoted to tending these helpless ones. You might think it easy to locate the bivouac, but Neal said not: he had searched innumerable times after stumbling on a column like this and was able successfully to follow up such an obvious clue only once in a hundred times.

A bit perplexed by the absence of soldiers guarding the procession, he began to prowl about in adjacent undergrowth and almost immediately shouted, "I've found the bivouac! It's here— only a few feet away, and all the soldiers are here, too. Oh, what great luck!" What he meant by "luck" could be ascribed to his professorial leanings: now the students could collect enough material for a year of study, whereas their little hand forceps were making only a paltry show in the bottles.

But then came the question: how could we deal with thousands of ants? We had rushed to Neal's position and saw what looked like a writhing black ball of life, about one foot in diameter, encompassing stalks of a small sapling and some twisting vines just above ground level. I would have thought this spectacle a sufficient lesson in itself, but apparently that was only a beginning. Neal said that the students could not only sort out the various kinds of prey but now also make a census of the different castes, as well as an estimate of eggs, larvae and pupae in relation to the adult population. Still, how could we approach that fiery mass?

Dries Jonkers stepped forward from the audience. This is the kind of challenge he enjoys: a physical engineering problem that stumps stupid biologists. He said that at We House we had some large plastic bags that could easily hold as many ants as Neal wanted. "I want them all," he answered. Dries said there were enough bags for that order. I don't remember what those bags were for, but they *were* large, much more capacious than the kind used for covering pillows.

Promptly we organized our strategy. The ants might chew their way through the thin plastic, so they must be chlorformed immediately. We would pour chloroform into the bags first and then dump ants into their gas chambers. There was still the problem of moving them from Point A to Point B. Dries suggested that Neal could wear a bag over each arm and use them as scoops, while the rest of us held the chloroform bags open to receive the castings.

Moon, still in his trusty boots, went close to the bivouac in order to cut the sapling and vines so that Neal would have a clear arena. This set up a panic at once. Soldiers swarmed out to avenge the disturbance. We would have only a few minutes before all but Moon had to retreat. Meanwhile we had girded Neal in his armor, tying the bags tightly above his elbows. Staunchly he advanced and struck.

After we had de-anted him for the second time that day, we took a look at the loot. Things had worked fairly well, except that the chloroform bags leaked—Dries hadn't counted on that! And the rest of us had quit while Neal was still scooping: we weren't quite so keen on being eaten alive. Rather disconsolately, Neal estimated that we hadn't gotten nearly all of them—perhaps only one third. "That means we may have missed the queen," he said.

Everyone left the swamp and I returned to the quiet of We House. Next day I located the bivouac again, nor far from its former position. When I reported that accomplishment to Neal several days later, his gloom deepened. "Then we *didn't* get the queen," he announced. "If we had, the rest of the ants would have become disorganized."

More than six months later I had an opportunity to visit Swarthmore again. The bachacs were happily traversing tubular highways that Neal had prepared for them. Just as if they were defoliating my okras, crossing the lawn and disappearing down tunnels, they forayed along well-learned plastic pathways to the rose-petal chamber and returned to their fungus cubicle.

"What about the army ants?" I asked.

"There they are," he said, pointing to two gallon jars. "We cleaned out all the sticks and leaves, and that is a pure collection of army ant ecology."

"But haven't your students sorted them out yet?" I persisted.

"This became so much better than I expected," replied Neal, "that I am saving them for just the right graduate scholar, whenever he comes along."

Chapter 18

BIRDS OUT OF REACH

"*P*ull! Pull, Brooke! God *damn* it, *pull!*" shouted Dries Jonkers. James Thomas had already called to me to pull, but I didn't hear him. He knew of my partial deafness but did not think it fitting to convey the urgency for pulling by raising his voice; certainly not by using strong language.

The scene of Dries's profane exhortation was, of course, our We House clearing. In fact I was standing on the gallery itself, holding two guy wires, when the not-lambent message reached my ears. This was the day on which we (subsequently they, for I was quickly retired) raised two towers for the canopy bird net, my chief joy in Bush Bush thenceforth.

I had quite a hassle with Leslie Spence to get this enterprise literally off the ground. Very early in our association he sensed (with absolute correctness) that my primary interest was birds. That might not be a good recommendation for a member of a virus team, but on the other hand it might be the best of credentials. We never worked this out to an end point. I still maintain that you must put birds first if you want to know how and when they acquire and then disseminate virus infections. Leslie believes that this is immaterial: as long as you collect a specimen from the bird at a known time and place, its viral or antibody content will give you a sort of flash photo of viruses at that instant. Gather enough such pictures, and you can piece together a panorama and assemble a chronology. Probably we are both right.

Anyhow, I began my bird-banding program in Bush Bush as a side line while studying the population crash of small mammals. Four nets at ground level in the immediate vicinity of We House caught an expectedly small number of birds, but a fair proportion of them reappeared in the nets regularly, and I began to feel I knew something about the denizens of that part of the forest.

At coffee Leslie used to ask, "When are you going to begin bleeding them?" Invariably I would answer, "I haven't got a sufficiently broad base line yet. Bleeding will result in the loss of some individuals, upsetting the population balance. If it is to be upset, I want to be able to appraise the deviation, and I can't do that until I know what the natural fluctuations are."

That was reasonable, but Leslie still thought it was an excuse. "You're just soft on birds," he summarized. Rather irreconcilably, I *am* soft on birds but can deal with them objectively at the same time. Elisha, having listened to Leslie's coffee talk in Port-of-Spain, was horrified when I collected the nest of a small flycatcher, mother and all, in British Guiana just as the eggs were hatching. "Brooke!" he gasped. "Can this be you?"

Another reason for my delaying tactics in Bush Bush was that at that time I had not yet learned to bleed birds from the jugular vein. Formerly (and in other locations) we had obtained specimens by cardiac puncture, intentionally "bleeding the birds out," a fatal procedure. Jugular bleeding, once mastered, leads to negligible mortality, but I did not want to practice on my We House friends, some of them now wearing bands for over a year.

In the end Leslie prevailed. Affairs progressed better than I had feared, and before long I considered myself a moderately proficient jugular expert. Small mammals having by this time virtually vanished, I expanded the ground-netting program to include more distant parts of the jungle, as well as the ramp across Petit Bush Bush Swamp. First thing I knew, I was almost fully in the bird business.

That improved my stature in Leslie's eyes to a considerable de-

gree, but he would never relinquish his position that any ornithological suggestion I made was derived from private interest; he
was probably correct. My proposal to erect towers for elevating a
canopy bird net was therefore met with polite conservatism such as
only Leslie can muster when he is against something. He was not
interested at all in my carefully prepared arguments about the additional things we might learn about viruses in treetops. His only
question was: "Can you guarantee that it will work?"

This man should have been a lawyer—or a lawyer as well as a
doctor, for he is a master in the profession he chose. He can find the
weak point in any proposition. Naturally in biological pursuits no
one can ever "guarantee" anything, as used to be possible in the old
physics and mathematics. Biological predictions are based on prob-
abilities only, though in many cases these odds are extremely inviting. The man who sells you life insurance when you are twenty can't
tell whether you will keel over half an hour after you have signed
the policy, but he knows that if you do ten thousand others won't.

"No," I answered. "I can give you no pledge, but if you ask me
if I *think* it will work, I can say only that I would not have suggested the plan unless I felt success bursting from my frontal lobes."

"What will it cost?" was his next gambit. I had no idea. The
budget was his province. I had drawn up some crude plans but
could not specify exact quantities or types of materials required,
because I did not know what facilities existed in Trinidad for erecting towers in places like Bush Bush, inaccessible to highways.
Tommy's spidery mosquito-catching platforms had been brought in
by boat and then lashed against trees, but I needed something self-
sustaining in the open, so that bird nets would not become entangled in branches.

It so happened that two of Tommy's three tree stations were about
to be disassembled. They had each been constructed of five individual ten-foot sections of triangular radio mast, fitting together at
the ends. Leslie asked me whether I thought these would do, provided they could be set up the way I wanted them. That would give
me only fifty-foot towers, whereas the canopy at We House went up

to about eighty or one hundred. "O.K., if that's the best we can manage," I said.

At a cocktail party Leslie learned from an engineering friend that it would cost Tr. $3,000 to erect the towers. "So that's that," concluded the Director. But Leslie is as soft as butter inside. While I thought the matter had ended, he continued to make inquiries. TV had just come to Trinidad, and now Leslie discovered that fifty-foot TV antennas could be bought for something like fifty dollars. These were in the form of telescoping aluminum pipes, again in ten-foot sections, that could be extended and braced permanently. "Do you think they would be suitable?" he asked me.

Now it was time to go into conference with Dries. His brilliant suggestion was that we combine the two sets of materials—sections of Tommy's radio mast with TV antennas on top. I became lost as he calculated the various stresses involved, length and angle of guy wires and so forth, but his eventual conclusion was that it would be practical to use two radio-mast sections below, boosting the tip of a TV antenna to seventy feet. That was practically touching the zone I wanted to tap, and in all gratitude I said, "Amen."

James Thomas was set to work, laying concrete foundations for radio-mast sections and shoring those supports with builders' scaffolding pipe. I can not elaborate on all the other things he did under Dries's direction. In short, Dries thought of everything, down to the last turnbuckle, as well as the manpower we would need on the Great Day and the position and function of each man.

I can claim credit for only one phase of the planning, this having to do with apparatus for raising and lowering a net. The TV antennas terminated simply at the end of the last pipe section. Obviously some sort of arm with dangling pulleys must extend at right angles from each of them. Once Dries understood what I wanted, he designed this detail as well.

Throughout the duration of these preparations, which lasted for weeks as James was at times called off the job to do more urgent things (at least the rest of TRVL considered them more urgent), I grew more and more apprehensive. I still could not see how it would

be possible to lift the extended TV antenna and set its base atop a
radio mast twenty feet tall. And then Leslie's foreboding use of the
word "guarantee" kept recurring to me. The more intricate the
project became—the more man-hours of our men were poured into
it—the greater became the necessity that it must not only work but
be a smashing hit.

Leon and I went out to Bush Bush the night before. It is superfluous to say that I did not sleep well. Early in the morning I set
out my usual ground nets, but things were inactive at that season.

About nine o'clock everyone arrived—Dries, James, Moon,
Mohan, Motilal, our field driver Singh and the five mosquito catchers. With Leon and me that made a baker's dozen, which as I have
already divulged was one too many.

The business of pulling or not pulling was critical not only to
raising of an antenna but also to the welfare of our personnel. As
the pole was extended and clamped, section by section, it had to be
steadied by members of the crew spread out in three directions
holding guy wires. From their stations they could not tell whether it
was vertical or leaning. Dries, James and Singh, working at the base
of the antenna itself, were the only ones able to judge. Should the
elongating pole be allowed to deviate too far in any direction, weak
aluminum would buckle and the whole contraption would collapse
on the central trio.

It was not a matter of passively holding onto a wire. As sections
were extended, and finally the entire antenna was raised twenty
feet to the top of the radio-mast substructure, one had to play out
the wire while retaining proper tension. Obviously this had to be
done evenly by the men stationed in each of the three directions.
That is why James became dance master and called out his cues to
the troupe.

Well, I did pull, just in time. Dries called a temporary halt, telling everyone just to hold on for a moment. He took the wires from
me and said, "You haven't looked at your ground nets recently.
Don't you think it's time to check them?"

By one of the strangest strokes in the annals of Natural History,
a column of army ants had chosen to pass directly under one of my

forest nets. These hunters are frequently attended by certain birds that profit by the commotion ants create among other insects. As the vanguard moves forward, all prey in its path is attacked. Some of the potential victims escape by scurrying or flying before the threat, thus exposing themselves to equally voracious and implacable feathered hunters. That particular net, having been all but idle for several weeks, now held an unprecedented nine birds!

I rushed back to We House for more bird sacks and then spent an absorbing hour banding and recording the catch. When I finished, I found Dries sitting quietly on the gallery, eating his sandwiches. The first tower stood as erect as a pine tree, all wires taut and snugly clamped. Nylon ropes hung to the ground from elevated pulleys. "We got along just fine—after you left," he commented.

Why should I complain? No question of vanity was involved, and I rejoiced instead. If they could do it once, the second tower must be already assured. My admiration for Dries's immediate grasp of requirements for this project now rivaled my awe of Leslie's sharp insights. If they had minds like steel traps, my endowment was more like a bird net—full of holes, though it did occasionally catch what I deemed a lovely idea. There was no question of my "assisting" further. After lunch the men duplicated their morning performance with great dispatch: a first experience enabled them to cut the time almost in half.

I was amazed, as well as delighted, to see everyone packing up to leave after completing the job in only one day. Somehow I had felt that the task was so huge that it would take a long time of struggle, and that all kinds of unscheduled difficulties would arise. I would not have been astonished if somewhere along the line they had come to an impasse and Dries had announced, "It can't be done."

Now Leon and I were left with the invention and it was up to us —and birds—to justify the confidence and labors of our peers. However we could not make an immediate test. First I had to get all the ropes in order, above all securing the ends so that none of them could get away. If one of them suddenly became overweighted on one side, pulling the opposite strand up through its pulley and out—the entire length falling to earth—the tower would have to be taken down to restore it. I would then simply have to run away to Tobago, or preferably somewhere more remote. I could not face a coffee hour at the lab after such a debacle. Anxiety on that score led to my tying exorbitant knots and wiring loose ends. I can proudly state that we never lost a rope.

The next chore was to install two aluminum rods that I had designed for carrying the net. These each bore a series of hooks, spaced at two-foot intervals, for receiving net loops, serving to spread the snare to its eight-foot width. By the time all these adjustments had been completed, day was at an end. We could have raised the net, but then bats would have given us trouble. I was tempted to court even bats, because morning seemed hideously far in the future, like a Christmas stocking. Fortunately Leon's announcement of supper diverted me, though I am not really a glutton.

When two people scarcely sleep, it is hard to tell who is the first one awake at dawn. We made short, early work of breakfast. After the net had been fixed to its hooks, we stood at opposite tower bases, each holding a rope. "Let's go," I called. Gingerly we began to haul, and slowly the poles lifted their insignificant burden. We had to be careful to work at the same rate, to keep the net horizontal and to balance strains between the two towers. Even then I was disturbed, for the kind of TV antennas we used were not designed for lateral stress; they were supposed to be solitary, each bearing only its own weight from above.

Today I can be amused at our original caution. Flimsy as the rig looked, it had an ample margin of safety for the work planned for it. Undoubtedly Dries had included that factor in his calculations. Later Leon and I used to whip the net up and down as rapidly as we could move it. True, the towers and guy wires did tremble and sway as we did so, but apparently we never came close to overtaxing any of the parts.

On that first morning the poles and net gradually went up and up until they seemed to touch the sky. At last there was a satisfying "thunk" as each pole touched its pulley. We fastened our individual ropes to respective radio masts and withdrew for the vigil. Now I could step back to get a perspective of the net in relation to its background. Confirmed disappointment: it wasn't nearly high enough! On either side of the corridor we had cut especially for this enterprise, crowns of matchwood trees attracted scores of birds during periods of blossoming and fruiting. James Thomas had judged these feeding areas to be about seventy feet up and visualized the net as spreading between them as a perfect baffle. I had been uncertain of his estimate. Now it was easy to see that those trees were twenty or thirty feet taller than that approximation. Birds could fly back and forth between the crowns without hindrance. The net might intercept only the accidental strays.

It was a long time before I had the nerve to ask Dries whether he thought we could make the towers higher by adding additional sections of ten-foot radio mast to the foundations. One section would help, two would be good, and three admirable. Dries was on my side, but he was a devotee also of practicability. He concluded that we had stretched things already to the limits of mechanical tolerance—and of security for working personnel.

Finally I got past this dead end to a slight degree. I wired two thin wooden poles—cut from saplings in the forest—to the aluminum ones in such a way that they would clear the pulleys. Leon and I were then able to spread a second net between them *above* the original net. Thus in effect we began tapping the atmosphere at a maximum height of seventy-eight feet, rather than seventy, at the same time having doubled the area available for reception of stragglers correspondingly less far removed from their normal flyways.

But that was many irritating months—punctuated by numerous satisfactions—later. "You got a bird, Doctor," became a familiar sound as I followed other quests. The first time I heard it was scarcely half an hour after the net flew on its trial run. I was working on a forest rat but dropped everything to rush outside. On high I could see a large bird floundering in the strands, though I could not identify its kind. It was mainly white, something like a domestic pigeon of mixed breed, but there were no pigeons hereabouts. One thing was already certain: I had never caught this sort of bird in a ground net.

Lowering the rig was a matter of letting ropes slip through our hands, the aluminum poles having sufficient weight to overbalance the system. Again Leon and I had to watch each other—or, rather, both ends of the net at once—in order to bring it down evenly. Moreover we could stop it at any chosen level. In this case the white bird had flown into the net's lowest trammel, so we lashed ropes to radio-mast foundations when the captive was at my shoulder height —a position most convenient for removing it.

Now, what can I possibly say about this bird that will place it in the minds of any save tropical American ornithologists? Other people will not have heard of cotingas. The "official" vernacular name, as coined by my friend Rodolphe Meyer de Schauensee in his *Birds of Colombia*, is Black-tailed Tityra. In Trinidad you can take your choice between G. A. C. Herklots' "Benedictin" and "Black-tailed Frog-bird," though I don't know where he picked up those terms: I never heard anyone use them, and when I asked Moon, Mohan and Motilal what they called the species, they were unanimous in calling it Magic Bird. Anyhow, it is a black and white kind of cotinga with some red naked skin about the face. One of its relatives is the Mossy-throated Bellbird, a fabulous denizen of the Northern Range to which I have already referred.

The Magic Bird was unable to utter a charm that would extricate itself. Instead it took the conventional line of biting to defend life that seemed on the point of ending. I bore a scar for weeks where it had punctured the skin of my hand and drawn blood. Sometimes I would look at that blemish in Port-of-Spain and sigh with nostalgic happiness. For this bird had exercised at least two true types of magic. In the first place it proved to one and all that the canopy net was functional. Secondly, it supported my contention that we might effect a wider coverage of the Bush Bush avifauna if we stopped neglecting treetops.

Leslie is a gentleman beyond the call of propriety. He could not be unaware of my elation when I reported the net's success, and he allowed me to congratulate my great fortune *ad libitum*. Had he been less tender, might he not have said, "What? Only one bird after all that trouble and expense?"

Fortunately the matchwoods were coming into bloom, and the trees began to fill with Palm Tanagers—olive-green birds with black wings that are common all over Trinidad, even in cities and towns, though they largely avoid jungle interiors. Now Leon and I developed a sort of wry-necked condition, for we could not go even so short a distance as to the latrine without peering upward and over our shoulders at the net. I suppose it would have sufficed if we had agreed to look once every twenty minutes and remain oblivious otherwise, but it was not in us to be so self-controlled. Our gazing

BLACK-TAILED TITYRA

became so habitual that we would both automatically glance at the net's position when we were leaving We House for the mainland, though we had taken it down only a few minutes before.

Palm Tanagers were a mainstay as well as a joy. Often they arrived in family groups of three or four, though single individuals became ensnared frequently also. A valuable trait of this species, from my point of view, is its sociability. Owing to the net's being too low, as I have already complained, I saw group after group of tanagers fly over it between the opposed matchwood crowns. But they are playful or pugnacious birds, whatever the reason for their constant chasing of one another. Let just one of them dart a bit low and get caught in the net, and the others might fly down to investigate, thereby entrapping themselves. On several occasions we lowered the net because of an observed entangled tanager, and by the time I was ready to fill a bird sack, I had to send Leon for additional sacks because other birds had followed and entered the net during its descent.

Often one can measure happiness only in retrospect, but I had no doubts about my emotional well-being while the matchwoods matured their feathery inflorescences and developed seed clusters. Early morning was the best time of day to be happy, corresponding to birds' moods. Because of bats we had to take the net down, or at least lower and furl it, at dusk. But the first crack of light found us struggling into clothing, slapping on mosquito repellant and running to our accustomed tower stations. Leon would then attempt to prepare breakfast, almost resigned to burning the bacon owing to my repeated calls for his help.

I had a constant fear that we might catch an Amazon Parrot. Those birds have beaks like metal shears. If the Magic Bird had given me a scar that I could contemplate with satisfaction, what could a parrot do? I decided that Amazons must simply be released, provided we could get them out of the net. What they might wreak on these expensive snares was another uneasy consideration that I often pondered, though I did not mention it to budget-minded Leslie. These birds were extremely common and inordinately fond of matchwood seeds. I ought to have caught them as freely as

Palm Tanagers. But at last I had to admit that the net was at a proper height, since parrots frequented the very tops of the trees and were therefore out of range.

On one occasion we did net a psittacine defector. I called to Leon to pick up several dish towels and come running. Perhaps I could swaddle the bird sufficiently to get it loose without suffering major injury to myself. As the net descended, the parrot flounced about in the particular trammel it had entered: it was too big—thank goodness!—to become engaged in small meshes designed for fly-catchers. Just as we got the net to the ground, the parrot flounced out, to my great relief, and flew squawking through the forest like an indignant hen, if hens could fly.

During the blessed period of matchwood burgeoning I kept a tally of canopy-net performance compared with captures from ground nets. In the best of times ratios ran two or three to one in favor of my pet, a statistic that I was ungentlemanly enough to point out to Leslie after each Bush Bush excursion. Then the bottom fell out and I became a less faithful reporter. The trees ripened their last seeds and reverted to being no more than casual aerial perches in a sea of similarly nonspecific perches spread out in all directions. Now the net caught birds that just happened to be going that-a-way, for there was no further lure to concentrate them. The ratio of efficiency compared with ground nets dropped to one to one—sometimes even worse.

A suggestion that I hardly dared breathe was that we ought to have a series of canopy nets—not just one. The matchwoods had given proof that aerial netting sites can be just as seasonal and selective as ground locations. After all, we had terrestrial nets in all kinds of situations—in deep forest, in forest clearings, at forest edges, and along the open ramp across Petit Bush Bush Swamp. These gave varying yields, each according to the time of year and its specific locus. Why not erect towers at several places, especially where other kinds of tree were dominant? Might we not then aspire to an all-year sampling of the high avifauna?

An alternative would have been to dismantle the towers and move them successively to currently favorable spots several times a year, bringing them back to We House in matchwood season. *That* thought I really could not refrain from pushing down into the subconscious. Dries reminded me of a fact that I had almost forgotten, regarding forest canopies. Near jungle boundaries the epiphytic flora of such umbrageous shields—bromeliads and the like—makes a great sweep almost to ground level in response to sunlight that can infiltrate these edges. Possibly canopy-dwelling birds follow a similar distribution. "Why not, then," he asked, "build new towers where you need to go up only fifty feet or even less? Then you could dispense with radio-mast foundations and actually adjust your TV antennas to heights appropriate to each site. Necessary labor would be greatly reduced, and these setups could be easily moved whenever you wanted to try to a new place."

Words of wisdom, indeed! In a way I wished he had uttered them sooner, though I think in any event I would have wanted the We House towers first because it was so nice to sit on the gallery and watch the matchwood scene.

In the long run (we erected no additional towers) I obtained an indirect sort of confirmation of birds' descending to lower levels at outer limits of the jungle. The We House net was of course well in the center of Bush Bush's northern extremity. It caught not only Magic Birds but also several other characteristically high-dwelling species. One day we hauled down a flycatcher that I had never before seen—a Sulphury Flatbill. On another occasion it was a Seven-colored Parrot (a very small kind of which I had no fear). Again, we netted a Jacobin Hummingbird, beautiful in blue and white, that normally feeds at the highest treetop nectaries. These species, along with Amazon Parrots, apparently recognized elevation for what it was and stayed upstairs even when the forest canopy curved to its dip at the island's perimeter.

But there was another category, which included Palm Tanagers—a group of species that would be caught with almost equal regularity in the canopy net and in nets stretched across Petit Bush Bush Swamp, right in the open (although adjacent to the jungle) but *not* at ground level within the forest. Several kinds of honey creeper fell into this peculiar classification, as did some swifts. It seemed as if what they recognized was not elevation but an external surface. From above, the canopy must look like a rolling green field, and where it gives way to swampland the field must appear to be continuous. These birds simply shun dark confines: they would not creep at the bases of reed stalks in a marsh, so why make an exception of subsurface jungle features?

That observation in itself would have been interesting enough for a prolonged study and an eventual dissertation. However, there were other phenomena equally revealing. For example, the most commonly netted bird at ground level in the forest was the Golden-headed Manakin. Because this species, with a drab olive female and a spectacular black and orange male, is generally considered to be more arboreal than terrestrial, I had looked forward to taking large numbers of them in the canopy net. But as it turned out, Golden-headed Manakins were one of the rarest of Bush Bush birds at the seventy-foot level, though they were captured with great frequency along the open ramp. This species, and others in its behavioral category such as the migrant Northern Waterthrush and resident White-flanked Antbird, seemed to recognize terra firma as such.

Finally, a restricted category that embraced two species of trogon —the Greater and the Lesser Yellow-bellied—and to some extent the Rufous-tailed Jacamar, was characteristic of intermediate levels in the forest, the so-called understory. I caught a few jacamars in forest ground nets, but more along the ramp, and none in the canopy net. All trogons, so long as I was on duty in Trinidad, were taken along the ramp!

I came to the conclusion that four distinct zones of avian habitation come to an intersection where forest meets swamp: canopy, understory, terrestrial sylvatic and terrestrial savanna. Is that pure ornithology without relation to TRVL's virology program? Perhaps . . . but you never can tell.

Chapter 19

BATS

Stratification of birds at various levels in tropical forests is by no means a unique phenomenon. The same kind of differential distribution can be observed in many groups of plants, frogs, insects and so on—even in bats to some extent. I am afraid I have said some things that might be construed as hostile toward bats. Nothing could be farther from my feelings: I love them. It is simply that bats and bird nets don't mix, if you happen to be seeking birds. And bats in Trinidad are to be revered more formally than Magic Birds and Silver-beaks that bite your hand; even insectivorous and fruit-eating species of *Fledermäuse* may be infected with rabies virus, though vampires show the highest rates.

The most unobservant visitor to the American tropics will at once be aware of bats, for many species are attracted to the very centers of even large cities. Houses are constructed to provide maximum ventilation, affording myriads of roosting places. Public buildings likewise are built on the open-air principle: bats have been found having their daytime siestas behind a church organ in Port-of-Spain. At dusk these fleet creatures swarm into the skies, weaving bewildering mosaics as they course after insects. One becomes almost mesmerized by the erratic show.

Fruit feasters may be less conspicuous where trees are absent or when they are not in season. However, those householders who attempt to raise mangoes or papayas in their yards are all too aware of such pests, sometimes losing the entire yield. Certain types of ornamental palm produce small seeds covered by a fleshy pulp that also attracts hordes of bats periodically as successive sprays ripen.

At the time I left Trinidad sixty-six species of bat had been recorded from the island, and this number will slowly increase as additional kinds are discovered. It is likely that all the common bats have now been collected and that new ones will represent nothing more than strays from Venezuela, where the fauna is considerably richer. Indeed one small bat, not known from Trinidad proper, was found in a hollow scaffolding pipe on an oilrig in the middle of the Gulf of Paria: perhaps it was on its way to Trinidad and would have completed the journey but for its capture.

Most of these bats are not seen by the urban public, since they frequent open country or forests. People are invariably astonished to learn that there are so many varieties. If they thought there was more than one, they would have said, "Two: big ones and little ones." It is, in fact, extremely difficult to tell bats apart in flight, and almost all information about them is derived from study skins and skeletons.

TRVL was only marginally in the bat business. A peculiar arbovirus called Tacaribe had been isolated from a Trinidadian specimen that was processed in the course of a routine survey of other kinds of mammal as well. Thus far Tacaribe virus has no known direct medical importance except that it is demonstrably related to Junín virus that causes hemorrhagic fever in man in Argentina. This disease is believed to be absent from Trinidad. Yet a potential danger may reside in Tacaribe's existence, and TRVL has continued to look at bats from that standpoint over the years.

Bat rabies is a virus disease, too, but it is not caused by an arbovirus, and the Trinidadian government maintains a special department to deal with that problem. However, because of a mutual interest in bats, TRVL offered some of its facilities to the government zoologist in charge of rabies studies. Thus I was privileged to become an auditor and spectator on the fringe of the chiropteran biologists' other world. The first of these was Mr. Arthur Greenhall. When he returned to the States, my second teacher became Mr. Robert Loregnard. Without those two, much of what I saw would have had little meaning.

Rabies is anything but an esoteric subject, by which I mean only that everyone has at least heard of it. Therefore I shall skim over this part of bat lore by mentioning that in Trinidad the disease is transmitted almost exclusively to cattle by vampire bats. They take blood from other sources, but for unknown reasons bovines alone develop clinical symptoms. The virus must at times be deposited in wounds on other hosts—horses, donkeys, dogs and human beings. Yet nothing happens, and no one knows why.

Furthermore, rabies virus can be found in other kinds of bat, particularly those species that share vampire roosts, which suggests that some kind of bat-to-bat virus transmission, not involving biting, may take place. It is all extremely mysterious, and at this juncture esoteric, after all. One must therefore be wary of handling *all* bats, particularly in manipulating individuals whose behavior seems in any way abnormal. That is another reason why I disliked them in bird nets. They get much more entangled than birds, and I used to chloroform them in the meshes before risking a two-handed struggle for their removal.

Trinidad has two resident species of vampire, the common and the spotted. The latter is rare and feeds more readily on birds—especially chickens—than on mammals. Common vampires are the ones that cause major trouble. They have interesting habits, knowledge of which enables two lines of attack to be raised against them. When they invade a particular herd of cattle, they are likely to select only one or two individuals for their repeated nightly libations. Wounds thus kept open become progressively more conspicuous, so that anti-bat agents know exactly where to strike: they simply paint these lesions with a strychnine solution at nightfall, and bats arriving soon afterwards are poisoned on the spot. Another ruse is to locate vampire roosts and destroy bats by smoking them out of their hollows. As the creatures emerge, they may be shot or captured in nets placed in front of exits. Roosts can readily be located by their characteristic odor. Semidigested blood, discharged as a tarry sort of feces, collects at the base of a roost and emits a strangely pungent, aromatic and slightly sweetish-smelling exhalation. Vampire bats usually produce only one young per year. It would seem possible to eradicate them by systematic destruction except that many roosts are either inaccessible or else so remote in forests that they escape control efforts. Hence the best that can be hoped at present is to keep vampires at a minimum in populated regions.

Robert Loregnard, the government zoologist, came to my office one morning and asked me to visit his lab. "We've got a collection of puzzling bats, and maybe you can help to explain what is happening," he said. "They are ordinary fruit bats, but some of them are bright yellow instead of brown. We have seen this phenomenon in past years, always at this same time." The bats had been caught in Port-of-Spain on the previous night, during a scheduled weekly operation that had recently yielded only "normal" specimens.

They were indeed yellow. These were two common species of *Artibeus*—the greater and the lesser Trinidadian fruit bats, widely distributed over the island. At first I thought they might be covered with pollen, but Robert said that the color would not wash off; he had already tried. My next idea was that the animals might have crawled all the way inside yellow fruits that they were consuming, mangoes for example, and dyed themselves all over. Robert quickly pointed out that it was not mango season, and he did not know of any other yellow fruit that was currently ripe. "Besides," he said, "these bats are yellow inside, too." He showed me a dissection of one specimen that disclosed a bright yellow hue in most of the tissues, especially fatty deposits.

This at once reminded me of carotene, precursor of Vitamin A. Recourse to long-disused textbooks led me to recommend the following: "Try dissolving the pigment in alcohol, chloroform and ether, and tell me what happens," I advised. Alcohol did not touch it, but the others leached it out. "Carotene it probably is, then," I concluded. What healthy bats those must have been! We never learned where they obtained their vitamin supply.

Vampire bats, fruit bats, insectivorous bats, nectar-feeding bats, lizard-eating bats and even fish-eating bats: all were present in

Trinidad, showing how widely these mammals have diverged from a remote ancestor that could not possibly have been omnivorous. If one wanted to draw parallels between each of these forms and a corresponding type of bird, one could name, in the foregoing sequence: African oxpeckers, tanagers, flycatchers, hummingbirds, hawks and herons. (The oxpecker is far from a perfect comparison, but I know of no bird that is as highly adapted for obtaining and drinking blood as vampires.) While these birds differ widely in external form, apparently as a necessary part of success in procuring their respective kinds of food, bats have managed the same type of behavioral radiation, accompanied by appropriate physiological adjustments, with a minimum of structural modification. Even *Noctilio*, the fish-eating bat, would not impress you with its moderately elongated hind toes and claws until *after* you knew that it uses them to scoop up guppies as it skims water surfaces.

Arthur Greenhall had worked on bats in practically all parts of Trinidad except Bush Bush Forest. After TRVL established a field station there, and particularly after We House was built, he urged us to collect as many specimens as we could catch. Possibly some species not yet recognized on this offshore island were hidden in the jungle. Apart from that, the ranges of even the commonest bats should be fully delineated, whereas Bush Bush still appeared as a blank on distributional maps. Arthur talked sometimes of coming out himself, to erect special types of open-ended cylindrical boxes that would invite bats to use them as daytime roosts. Then one could simply make the rounds from time to time and easily gather disturbed specimens as they dropped out into butterfly nets. This plan never materialized, owing to Arthur's departure, and I was left on the gallery to watch bats in the evening and wonder what and who they were.

I soon found the notion of collecting them distasteful. The ones that flew about We House at dusk were charming little things that sometimes caught mosquitoes a foot in front of my nose. I could not actually see them do this, but it was clear to me that I acted as mosquito bait by sitting there, and the "worse" mosquitoes were, the more confiding became my bats. At Simla, Don Griffin showed us a remarkable slow-motion film of bats catching prey in flight. They do not accomplish this with their mouths, flycatcher fashion, but first enfold the victim in a membraneous wing. It would seem to me that they must then tumble to the ground, but transfer to a gaping mouth is effected with hardly the loss of a wingbeat. Spread sails from the two arms obviously make much more efficient snares than one pair of small jaws. Considering that the flight of many insects is irregular, one must surmise that such hunting tactics could not be improved upon. Why haven't birds found this out?

As I roamed the forest I gradually became familiar with a few facts of bat life. Indeed on that first visit with Wil Downs, when I saw the green *Ampullaria* egg masses in the swamp forest, he pointed out a number of strangely cut palmetto leaves that he called self-constructed bat shelters. Three or four inches from the center of diverging leaflets, bats had partially severed the midribs so that leaflets remained green but now hung down in the form of a protective tent. Afterwards I found such altered leaves in innumerable other places—you can recognize them as far as the eye's limits. The majority had been abandoned, but now and then you could peer from below and see a cluster of four or five small hanging creatures. Arthur said that several kinds of diminutive bat have learned this camping trick, one of the most common being the Yellow-eared Bat.

Another set of Chiroptera that became favorites of mine was a colony of Greater Two-lined (or Sac-winged) Bats. (I learned later that this species and its congener, the Lesser Two-lined, were my We House friends.) My affection derived from the fact that this group, which varied at different times from four to seven or eight individuals, could be counted upon to roost in the buttressed recess of a huge silk-cotton tree along my mammal trap line, not far west of the latrine. They were engaging enough in themselves, but whenever we had visitors and I happened to be showing them around, Two-lined Bats were a sure-fire attraction.

These little animals displayed a combination of tameness and nervousness that I became able to judge accurately. As we approached the silk-cotton tree, I would caution everyone to walk

slowly and let me take an advance look. When I had located the
colony (for they shifted about slightly), I could direct attention to
the point where bats would appear. Within the buttress they were
almost invisible. As soon as I gently rustled a stick near them, the
tiny beasts obligingly either scuttled or flew a few feet upwards
into plain view on the open trunk. Had they scattered into the
forest, there wouldd have been no show at all. Now all binoculars
(most of our guests carried them) clearly brought out all details of
marking and behavior at close range—two parallel wavy white lines
along the black back, big ears, snout unadorned with a "nose leaf"
or flaps, and a palpitating stance reflecting indecision whether or
not to take further flight.

Actually I did not have to enter the forest to seek roosting bats—
we had them right in the We House clearing, and I am not referring
to my mosquito-catching companions. Leon, in his enthusiasm for
gardening, rapidly cluttered up the place with all sorts of tubers,
shoots and cuttings that he picked up from friends. Thus it was not
long before we had a line of thriving young plantain "trees." These
are relatives of the banana, although the fruit converts little of its
starch to sugar and is therefore commonly cooked as a potato.

An upward-thrust spike from the crown of a plantain eventually
reveals itself as a tightly rolled column that must now unfurl. How
that complicated structure can be elaborated in the heart of a
plantain trunk remains one of the wondrous mysteries of botany to
me. Anyhow, the terminal part of a spike first expands into a
tubular trumpet, and after further growth the two sides of the
leaf are able to spread apart from their supporting midrib. By this
time the leaf begins to arch away from the vertical. It then goes
through successive stages of rapid maturity and senescence, for
development from shoot to fruit in these fantastic plants takes less
than a year.

In shaded tropical forest glades one often sees bats flying at all
hours of the day. Not so in Port-of-Spain or across open savannas
such as Nariva Swamp. I was therefore aroused one noon to observe a flittering bat near the cocorite palm in front of the gallery.
As I watched, it quickly disappeared somewhere within the foliage
of Leon's largest plantain tree. Naturally I was after it immediately.

At once I found a cluster of seven or eight batlets, hanging from the midrib of a leaf that had just achieved the horizontal stage of its eventual decline. They were hooked up, in the usual posture, by claws of their feet and thumbs, gathered in such a dense row that it was hard to count them exactly. I had by this time yielded to requests for occasional specimens, so I went to fetch my butterfly net. One or two less would not irreparably impoverish this group, and they might not be here tomorrow if I temporized now. A swoosh of the net yielded me a pair, which I promptly chloroformed.

This was a species I had not seen previously. Like so many others, it was small—much tinier than one would have judged after seeing it in flight. The animals bore conspicuous "nose leaves," strange flaps projecting upward from the snout, and had two light facial stripes leading back to the ears. Use of Goodwin and Greenhall's *Review of the Bats of Trinidad and Tobago,* published by the American Museum in New York, led me to identify them as Little Brazilian (or Pygmy) Bats, *Artibeus cinereus.*

The remaining bats had naturally scattered when I swept the net at their aerie. However, next morning they were back, and for some weeks I could rely on finding them under leaves of one or another plantain tree bordering the clearing. Inspection of many leaves disclosed evidence that these unsuspected guests had been with us for a long time. (I'm glad Tommy did not discover them first.) They did not need to bite sides of a leaf, to make it droop in tent style, for there was always at least one shelter in a suitably horizontal pose. Nevertheless the bats' claws scarred tender tissues of each temporarily favored midrib, leaving behind hundreds of small blackened puncture marks. That enabled me to make· a retrospective chart of where Pygmies had lurked before a careless one revealed their presence. Apparently Leon's plantains had been their dormitories for more than a month.

Bachacs put an end to this idyll. Arriving at We House one day, we found the trees stripped. That seemed to make little difference to plantains, which providently reclothed themselves with leaves in a trice, but I never saw the Pygmies again. Meanwhile, other bats inhabited new-forming leaf trumpets. When vertical spikes had uncoiled to a diameter of about one inch, they became ideal retreats for an even tinier and much more remarkable species. This was the Brazilian Disk-winged (or Sucker-footed) Bat, *Thyroptera tricolor*. The alternative names combine to describe the total adhesive equipment of this creature—suckers on all four extremities that enable it to hang not by claws, in the usual manner of bats, but by pneumatic devices. You must examine the inside of a young plantain or banana leaf to appreciate how smooth it is. Nothing short of suckers could give anything else but a snail purchase on such surfaces. For yet another time, but far from the last, I was impressed by bats' powers of adaptation following a minimal structural change. I do not belittle their accomplishments by any means—it may have taken a million years or more for those little suckers to develop—but these "disk-winged" creatures still look superficially like all other bats in creation.

Leon's plantains must have loomed as veritable modern motels, with spacious twin double beds, to *Thyroptera*. Plantains and bananas are both foreign to Bush Bush Forest. The commonest natural roosts for these bats are species of *Heliconia* (which harbored my ponerine ants) and some of their relatives. But those plants bear much smaller leaves which, in their unfolding, present vertical trumpets that could accommodate at best two bats at a time. More often, the daytime sleepers probably occupy single beds. In any case, whether solitary or in Leon's lavish quarters, the bats must find new homes at almost every dawning, because leaves in this stage of growth are at their most rapid period of expansion. What was a safe cylindrical sheath yesterday has now flared out into a broad blade, useless for further concealment.

Flying bats have exceptionally few enemies. A few kinds of hawk, in separated parts of the world, have become adapted specifically as bat catchers, but in general a bat on the wing may be considered as free as any being on earth. At rest, however, bats face shorter odds. Seclusion in caves and hollow trees must protect them from many a direct onslaught. Even here they are not immune to predators such as snakes and opossums that press their searches to all but the deepest recesses. In the form of a Disk-winged Bat one can read a kind of evolutionary predation pressure dial: nothing can be more clear than that need for daytime sanctuary has molded it. As yet, so far as I know, no one has discovered their secret invention for hiding on polished surfaces, and I feel rather a blabber to mention it here, lest a raccoon be listening.

In due course my ground nets caught several day-flying bats, whether or not they should have been abroad at that time. When I at last extended the canopy net to its double capacity, I was so pleased with myself that I allowed it to stay up all night, bats or no. As a result, I brought a series of specimens to the lab that aroused great interest. None was new from Trinidad, but most were considered rare and all added to known ranges of familiar species.

In my nosy way, I always wanted to know what they were. Here I ran into a most annoying practice of the bat people. They can tell bats apart and give them Latin names, but they don't know quite what to call them in plain English. I regard this as a pity, for it seems to preclude poetry that might be directed to this attractive tribe if members bore short, rather than painfully descriptive, names. "Hark, hark, the lark (*or* long hind-clawed herald) at heaven's gate sings!" breaks acceptable meter as well as several other hallowed aesthetic tenets.

Robert Loregnard, having succeeded Arthur Greenhall at the bat lab in TRVL, determined to take advantage of my canopy rig. "Bring your own nets," I cautioned, "and Leon and I shall show you how to operate the mechanism. Other than that you may do whatever you like. The more you do the better, as long as you tell me about each discovery."

He took me so literally at my word that the first thing I had to do was disarm his five assistants of guns and revolvers when they arrived at We House late one afternoon. These are acknowledged bat-collecting devices, and I did not mean to defy convention, but meanwhile I refused to allow howler monkeys to be scared out of our cherished reservation. The gallery became a temporary arsenal as the men deposited firearms and went about more pacific chores, arranging not only nets for the canopy rig but a host of ground nets that I had not envisaged.

Alas! One net was set exactly where little mosquito destroyers used to attend my comfort. This was the night on which I learned that they were greater and lesser Trinidadian Two-lined (*or* Sac-winged) Bats. It was hard to persuade myself that I was being compensated by other information, lavish though this turned out to be. Bat lore in general is what I most sought, but these experts filled me in first with lists of what they found. Actually they returned a second time, bringing their combined catch to a total of thirty-two bats of thirteen species, of which seven kinds were represented by only one individual. Perhaps a list of names, provided I leave out the word "or," would still show you how far from larks these creatures reside in poetry: Lesser Two-lined, Lesser Round-eared, Lesser Long-tongued, Greater White-lined, Greater Trinidadian Fruit, Lesser Trinidadian Fruit, Little Barbadian Fruit, Little Black, Greater Moustached, Fringe-lipped, Short-tailed Fruit, Yellow-eared, and Central American White-lined Bats! Among these the "Little Black" would seem to me to have greatest potential for place in a sonnet, though I will mount no dispute against anyone who cares to challenge that timorous opinion.

My sporadic daytime net captures had included quite a number of other species which I shall not name because their titles are equally odious. Robert Loregnard reacted to his two excursions, that brought the combined Bush Bush list to twenty-eight kinds of bat, with inventive enthusiasm. "What we need now," he said, "is a white background behind your canopy net. This should not be too high—about halfway up. It is especially hard to net insectivorous bats, for their echo-locating abilities seem often to enable them to detect even fine nylon strands, whereas fruit bats blunder into such snares more like birds. But if we put up something like a basketball backboard, painted white, and shine a flood lamp upon it, *that* should attract insects, which in turn lure bats. Then all we shall need will be your net between the board and the light."

Some months after I left Trinidad I received a letter from Dries which read, in part, "Unknown vandals demolished one of your bird-net towers. In your absence we have decided to take down the entire rig and store it at the lab for possible future use elsewhere." They had not consulted Robert, obviously.

Chapter 20

SNAKES

One is invariably questioned about snakes of the tropics, particularly monstrous ones hanging from jungle trees. Ignoring the latter fantasy, I still must give a disappointing answer—that is, the listener who wants his blood curdled won't receive satisfaction from me. The only way I was disappointed was not in experiencing narrow escapes but in seeing too few snakes. A day's walk through Bush Bush Forest frequently turned up none at all. On the average, I think I could see as many, perhaps more, snakes during a Pennsylvania hike in summer as would flee at my approach in Trinidad over similar mileage.

Not that they weren't there, or that some weren't dangerous: Trinidad supports thirty-eight species of snake, of which four are poisonous and two are large constrictors. But all fear man who, in his prejudice, has slaughtered them, regardless of species, at every opportunity. I think the angriest I ever saw Wil Downs was one morning when we were driving to Bush Bush. Near Sangre Grande a car in front of us deliberately swerved to run over a harmless snake, whereupon the car stopped and four East Indians got out to look at it—probably to give it a final coup. Wil stopped, too, and ran up to the writhing creature.

"It's living, it's living!" the men cried in terrified falsetto unison.

"Of *course* it's goddam well living you ignorant fools!" bellowed Wil. Before their incredulous eyes he put his foot gently behind the snake's head, grasped it by the neck and dropped it neatly into a cloth sack. But his hands were trembling. The snake continued "living" for a while in a cage at the lab, but died of internal injuries (to some of which we contributed with hypodermic needles).

Probably the attitude of true woodsmen toward snakes is a good index of the danger they present. Rubber boots reaching to the knee are standard equipment in Trinidadian forests, since most snake bites result not from deliberate attack but from carelessness on the part of both biter and bitten: the serpent should have moved, and the man should have been watching more sharply. However, if a hunter is stalking game, it is difficult for him to keep his eyes always on the ground. Once stepped on, a snake has no recourse but to strike back, and as a rule the only mark it can reach is a leg. Even nonvenomous snakes will bite under such circumstances, and they can sometimes inflict painful wounds regardless of their nontoxic nature. In the excitement that follows such encounters, the snake may disappear before the victim has time to see what kind it was: thus he does not know whether he has been poisoned or not. The number of man-hours spent in jungles of Trinidad by woodcutters and huntsmen every year must be incalculable; yet thanks to rubber boots the annual death rate from snake bite on the island is less than one.

To tell my most harrowing story first, I must report our capture of a fer-de-lance in the yard at We House. This venomous species is known as the "mapepire" to local inhabitants. One afternoon Leon was raking leaves near the cocorite palm when he uncovered a small snake that did not retreat as it ought to have done. He called me to see it, and I observed a thickish, mottled creature which later proved to be fourteen-and-a-half inches long. We were both wearing ordinary sneakers and khakis—perfect marks for offensive fangs—but the snake just lay there, eying us as if unconcerned. Its head had a rather ominous triangular shape, but I knew that some kinds of nonpoisonous species are made that way also.

"Watch it while I get my butterfly net," I told Leon. Taking the rake from him, I nudged the snake, which obediently entered the net that I presented conveniently for its reception. In another moment the bag of the net was lowered into a chloroform jar. When the animal was dead beyond all doubt, I examined its jaws through the Optivisor. Fangs! Movable fangs, hinged to the front of the upper jaw, lying against the roof of the mouth in sheaths of mucous membrane, but easily exposed and reflected forward with a pair of forceps.

So that was our "narrow escape." Somehow sneakers and butterfly nets seem foreign to such a tale of adventure, but it's the best I can do. I did indulge in a rather sobering reflection. A baby mapepire must have had parents, and since babies have not yet had time to travel very far, those parents might still be nearby. Not to mention the likelihood that this was one of a litter. Adults reach a length of eight feet. Were we, then, surrounded by the enemy? I asked Leon whether he was frightened. He was not, nor was I, though this may have been only foolhardiness, I really don't know. We continued to wear sneakers and khakis and to go about our pleasures as if all other mapepires would be as friendly as this one had been.

Self-styled "snake experts" abound among country people, even though professional herpetologists often find it necessary to make painstaking counts of scale rows before arriving at a specimen's correct name. I was not amazed, therefore, when an argument arose between James Thomas and Motilal regarding our mapepire. I had shown them both the curved fangs, leaving no doubt as to the general character of the beast. But Motilal insisted that it was not a fer-de-lance but a young bushmaster—another, even larger, kind of mapepire common in the Northern Range. To date bushmasters had not been recorded in Bush Bush Forest, and I was inclined to agree with James. True, we had not done much snake-collecting here, and it was conceivable that both species existed in our forest. Mohan once killed a snake after it had struck his rubber boot, and this proved to be a fer-de-lance, but that was rather a slim basis for making generalizations. When my We House specimen was finally "keyed out" at the lab by Raymond Manuel as *Bothrops atrox*, Motilal had to yield to James Thomas' superior woodcraft in this instance.

Confusion regarding identity of young snakes is often excusable, for in early stages they may look quite different from hoary parents. Our little mapepire certainly showed none of the geometric back markings that it would have developed later, and its ventral surface was finely checkered in a pattern utterly foreign to adult decoration. It is in such cases that herpetologists' scale counting must be invoked. On the other hand, I suspect that Motilal may never have seen a true bushmaster, for he was not a "well-traveled" Trinidadian like James. Nor could I enter the argument, having seen neither species. All my walks in the Northern Range were unattended by poisonous snakes. One day, having stopped the car to look at an unfamiliar bird, I found the dried carcass of a bushmaster that must have been run over weeks before. It was about five feet long—less than half the twelve-foot maximum size allowed by confirmed measurements. And that ended my contact with pit vipers in Trinidad.

As for boas and anacondas, I had even worse luck—and ran into equal degrees of controversy when the field crew reported such creatures. Arriving at the forty-six-mile post one afternoon, I found our men just leaving after their day in Bush Bush and noticed at once that James was carrying a gun. TRVL had established strict rules against this practice, for it would be all too easy for someone to shoot a dove and claim afterwards that he had mistaken it for a jaguar. This time James assured me that there was a "big wheel" in Petit Bush Bush Swamp. My ears had not failed me, though the orthography was wrong. Anacondas, or water boas, are locally called "huilles." I suppose that the sight of a huge huille would frighten anyone, and since James was at that time repairing the ramp, he was entitled to carry some form of self-protection. However I had looked into the subject and found that anacondas normally eat other snakes, such as boa constrictors, in addition to caymans, freshwater turtles and fish. Not a mammal—let alone human beings—on the list. I told him immediately that he must not shoot the huille, whereupon he followed his first claim by stating that he had seen a great cayman as well. Those alligatorlike reptiles *can* be dangerous, but I was a bit sceptical because he had not mentioned that peril first.

He said he judged the snake to have been twenty feet long. That, too, sounded unlikely to me. It was not impossible, for specimens of twenty-five-foot extent have been documented. But it is rare, at least in Nariva Swamp, for anacondas to have a chance to attain that dimension. Annual grass fires in the dry season probably destroy enormous numbers of snakes as well as many other slow-moving inhabitants. Climatic cycles sometimes lead to a succession of wet years during which fires can not spread widely. In such benign times small huilles can add a few feet of extra length to their statures, though the damp respite ends long before they become gargantuan.

Motilal had been gossiping with East Indian melon planters at the forty-six-mile post and did not hear our discussion. Arrived at We House, he at once began setting up ground bird nets, including those across Petit Bush Bush Swamp. On his return he remarked, without undue excitement, that he had seen a "big wheel" along the ramp. "How big?" I asked. "About ten feet, Doc," he ventured. So James's specimen had been cut in half! At least I could not doubt that they had seen the same creature. After years of anaconda-free traffic in this restricted locale, was it likely that *two* would reach crossroads on the same day?

In practically every place I have lived there has been a unique individual who seemingly can smell snakes. Such was John Dunstan, an employee at the Arima textile factory in Trinidad. You could almost count on John to have a collection of boa constrictors, among other prizes, in his menagerie. Mostly he did nothing special with them—he just liked having them around for a while and then he let them go. When he wanted others, he simply went out and found them. This was very handy for Tommy, who liked to collect parasitic ticks and mites from any reptile whatsoever, and it helped me, too, at a time when I was gathering a battery of varied serum specimens for rather complicated purposes.

Dr. Bernard Weitz, of the Lister Institute in England, had volunteered to prepare a specific *anti*serum by injecting rabbits with any *primary* serum submitted to him. A set of antisera could then be used to identify an unknown serum after fractions of the unknown had been combined with each member of the set: reacting solutions, brought gently together, formed a precipitate at their interface, while the others remained clear. At TRVL we wanted to know what kinds of animal were fed upon by various species of mosquito. Through Dr. Weitz's cooperation, it would be possible for us to send him dried blood, squeezed from mosquito stomachs onto snippets of filter paper, which he could dissolve and test, *if* he had all the appropriate rabbit antisera on hand. Therefore we became blood-thirsty for bats, porcupines, monkeys, birds, snakes and every other creature with a heart. Boa constrictors seemed to fit this order because of their size, and John Dunstan was obviously our man.

"Yes, I've got two nice ones," he said, after I had closed the gate to prevent his pet deer from escaping. "You just grab that one, while I keep this one quiet." He had opened a small cage, and I saw a broad head, at the end of a sinuous, serpentine neck, leveled at me. Following orders, I grasped the sleepy reptile, which at once confidingly wrapped itself around my arm and neck. It was a shame that Owen Olivier and I had to exsanguinate it at the lab.

A beautiful smaller snake, the rainbow boa, occurs commonly in Trinidad, and then there was the Cook's tree boa which consumed one of my banded tropical house wrens. The latter snake is relatively slender for a boa and, besides, has a horrible disposition, never becoming tame in captivity. Tommy and I encountered one at the edge of the We House clearing, while exploring at night with head lamps just for "kicks." We might have had a more serious purpose, for he had just received a long-distance telephone call from someone at the Seattle World's Fair who wanted Tommy to drop everything and collect elater beetles for their exhibit of animal bioluminescence. You don't need head lamps for that search, so perhaps my first statement was accurate; we were simply having fun. Two ruby eyes glowed at us from a low heliconia plant, and we tried to attach them to a body. They could belong to a moth or spider, a tree frog, or perhaps a murine opossum. Tommy's vision resolved the rest of the creature first. "Snake!" he declared, pouncing upon it. I held a sack as he stuffed it in. Then, believing that the bag was securely tied, I began to back out of the thicket. Suddenly I felt my hand seized in an uncomfortable manner. The Cook's tree boa had reversed itself in a trice, and in the darkness I had tied the sack around its neck, leaving the head free. We *did* have fun!

Bertie Sam picked up a rainbow boa one week end and dutifully brought it to the lab on Monday. We already had plenty of snake serum for Dr. Weitz, so the question of what to do with this specimen required several coffee sessions to settle. Ultimately we decided on an experiment that had a fundamental bearing on virus research in Trinidad and in neighboring tropical countries. We had included snakes and other reptiles in our surveys for viruses and antibodies, but all results had been negative. However, some workers elsewhere reported otherwise. In Brazil several odd viruses had been recovered from lizards, while in Panama those creatures were said to yield antibodies to certain viruses of known importance.

Most pertinent to our problem were investigations in the United States on western equine encephalitis (WEE) virus in garter snakes. During the winter, mosquito populations are largely killed off, and hibernating individuals had not been found to contain virus. Yet the following summer WEE virus reappeared in mosquito and vertebrate hosts. Where had it been during the long, frigid months?

Now it was found that garter snakes have a unique way of responding to injections of WEE virus: they do *not* respond. That is, warm-blooded vertebrates—birds and mammals—circulate the virus for a few days and then become immune, after which mosquitoes can no longer become infected by feeding on them. Snakes, on the contrary, became viremic and *stayed* viremic. The virus did not kill them, as it would a bird or mammal that built up no resistance against it. Instead, the pathogen seemed to have a free time, multiplying in the cold-blooded host without hindrance and reciprocally causing no harm.

The workers reasoned that perhaps a snake, infected in the fall, could hibernate and then emerge in the spring still circulating virus, thus restoring it to the general environment after a new generation of mosquitoes had filled their bellies from its capillaries. For some mosquitoes do bite snakes as well as other creatures. The experiment in the States had been successful, and thus at least one potential mechanism for overwintering of WEE virus had been demonstrated.

In Trinidad we faced a related problem centered on the survival of *eastern* equine encephalitis (EEE) virus during long dry seasons when mosquito vectors were sharply reduced in numbers. Then we could find no current infections among the small remaining numbers of suitable mosquito hosts, but again EEE activity would resume with onset of the rains. Could snakes have anything to do with the case?

Bertie's rainbow boa was an ideal subject for such a test, being docile and large enough to contain a conspicuous heart for probing needles to find. As I left Trinidad the experiment was still in progress, but already the boa's EEE viremia had extended considerably beyond that which would have followed infection of ordinary laboratory animals. And I hasten to add that it was in perfect health, eating white mice by the dozen and apparently not in the least discomfited by weekly cardiac punctures. So that all sounded very promising except for the nagging thought: why hadn't we recovered viruses from wild snakes?

Adventures with serpents are usually innocent enough, even though they can give one a nasty turn. Wil visited us once when the boat line had dwindled to a muddy trough and it was necessary for Moon to push the boat from behind. Decaying fish, littering the banks, attracted scores of sarcophagid flies, which are one of Wil's hobbies. He repeatedly called to Moon to stop while he swung a small net over the juiciest fish. During one of these halts, a snake's head emerged from the opaque water, six inches from Moon's bare knee. I think they both were given nasty turns, judging by the way they gave ground to each other.

The population crash of small mammals in Bush Bush Forest could have been abetted by several kinds of snake known to be rodent eaters. Among these the commonest was a large black species with a yellow tail. Perhaps it was not really common, for it is possible that I kept seeing the same one in various parts of my study area. This animal was not excessively shy and often let me watch it even after it had seen me. I doubt, however, that snakes were basic to the disappearance of rodents and murine opossums, for there had been no sudden plague of serpents and their density—at least so far as direct observation is concerned—was low.

Often while sitting on the gallery I would notice a slight movement in the bank of heliconias across the yard, as if one of the stems had wavered. On a windless day this would be a signal for me to go over and say "Hello" to an ashy whip snake that lived there. It was an attractive wraith with an excessively long and narrow head, the five-foot body being also extremely thin. A black stripe extended from its jaws and below the eye to the neck. In this species the strategy of escape is to stay still. Thus I could go right up to it and look into its nostrils through the Optivisor if I wanted to. I suppose it lived on insects, but whether it sought its prey or allowed unsuspecting arthropods practically to walk into its mouth I don't know. At rest it was impossible to find, and so hawks probably passed it by. There were plenty of snake-eating hawks about, incidentally. One, a Double-toothed Kite, used to perch on a canopy-net tower until the day I caught, bled and banded it. Snake hawks were therefore allies of rodents, as opposed to their mammal-eating relations. To a rat, however, a hawk must be a hawk, just as the sons of Adam lump all snakes together.

At the other extreme from anacondas were worm snakes, tiny creatures only six inches long and half as thick as a pencil. Leon found one in the forest just as it was crawling under a leaf. This was the rarer of the two Trinidadian species, being recognizable by its pink spot at each end. The other kind is white only on the head. Both are burrowing eremites, dark brown in color, with small eyes, blunt tails and mouths that look too minute and feeble to ingest anything. Apparently they succeed in feeding on termites, ants, millipedes and similar fragile ground inhabitants. While walking home from the lab one Sunday morning, I saw a hefty gardener beating the lawn frantically with a great stick: his mower had uncovered—guess what?

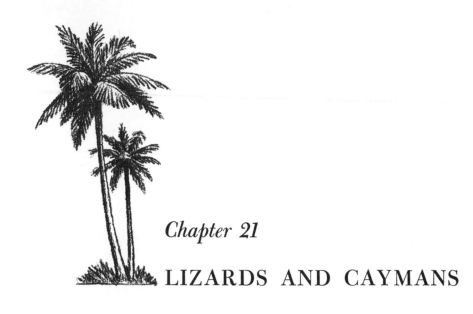

Chapter 21

LIZARDS AND CAYMANS

*N*egative virological results with lizards did not disturb us until we heard opposing reports from Brazil and Panama. Geographically we were sitting directly between those two places. Obviously the shoe was on *our* foot, and we would have to learn to walk, whether it pinched or not.

Tommy had already made a thorough study of these creatures, so we knew all about the kinds to be found in Bush Bush. The largest one, *Tupinambis nigropunctatus,* is called "teju" or "tegu" in dictionaries of the English language, though in Trinidad it is known equally simply as a "matte." This powerful reptile, reaching a length over two feet, roams the forest by day in search of anything that can be eaten. When the baby corbeau was killed, Moon suggested that a matte might have been responsible, though at the time my suspicions were directed more to larger predators such as dogs or opossums. However a later episode brought me to Moon's side, so far as inclusive possibilities were concerned. He was making rounds of Hav-a-hart mammal traps one afternoon and found that one had caught a matte. The beast seemed to be dead, perhaps from heat prostration on that hot day of the dry season, so he reached in to remove it. Thereupon his hand was gripped in iron jaws that refused to let go. As he gave his account after returning in bandages from the hospital in Sangre Grande, he had had to kneel on the lizard and use all his might to pry open those tongs with a stick.

Indeed the sun had probably given the monster extra strength, because the reactivity of such cold-blooded animals is regulated by external temperatures. At the lab we kept a few mattes in outdoor cages, and I used to handle them quite easily at six o'clock in the morning after they had been chilled overnight. Of course I wore heavy leather gloves to do that—just in case—but there was never any serious struggle.

That was in the era before We House had been built, and I would leave Port-of-Spain very early in order to spend a maximum number of hours in Bush Bush. We were conducting a special study of mosquitoes' feeding preferences by exposing various kinds of animal in individual traps and analyzing the species of biters attracted to each. A captive matte would be confined in one trap, an *Oryzomys,* a *Heteromys* and a *Zygodontomys* in each of three others, and several white mice in a fifth. As might be suspected, the four species of rodent were fed upon by roughly the same sorts of mosquito, though even among these we could discern some that, for example, liked the taste of white mouse better than, say, *Oryzomys.* The divergence was much more marked between lizard and rodent bait. However, as might *not* have been suspected, the matte attracted just about the same total number of mosquitoes as did rodents, though the various species were represented in different proportions. Furthermore the kinds were all the same. Thus we would conclude that mosquito Species A vastly preferred to feed on lizards, though it sometimes would bite rodents, while Species B indulged reverse tastes. That was a highly important finding, for it meant that viruses could be transferred between vertebrate host populations of widely separated relationships. If this were not true, certain viruses might be isolated in some obscure reservoir host and never have a chance to "escape" into more general circulation.

Mattes always looked black with yellow markings to me, but the name, "*nigropunctatus,*" would have it the other way round. Their thick bodies end in blunt tails: yet with cumbersome forms they could run through the forest at high speed. Often they would wait until one was almost upon them—perhaps they were basking—before taking off with great crashing of leaves and underbrush. Our visitors were always alarmed, having snakes in mind. Frequently one could not see the source of commotion, and I had to be at my most persuasive to reassure them.

Usually such trailside disturbances were caused by a smaller and more common lizard, the so-called jungle runner, *Ameiva ameiva*. This species is found all over the island, as opposed to mattes, which are partial to woodland cover. In fact Arthur Greenhall told me that mattes and mongooses have identical feeding habits and are therefore intolerant of each other. We had no mongooses in Bush Bush, and I never saw a matte in the Caroni Swamp where mongooses abound, so perhaps there is something in this hypothesis.

"Jungle" runners are ill named, for they swarmed on the neatly tended lawn of TRVL as freely as anywhere else. I frequently watched them at close range as I sat at my desk and they foraged directly under my office window. These lizards are far more trim than mattes, with long, pointed tails and a splash of bright green on forward parts of their brown bodies. Large ones approach two feet in length. They move over the grass with a jerky gait, bobbing their heads at each step. I could see that after each bob a slender tongue was extended to "taste" the ground. I don't know whether jungle runners hunt by sight also, but I suspect that tongues are their mainstay in finding food. Nevertheless, their vision must be good, for otherwise they could not dare run so fast. Hunting forays were constantly being interrupted by lightning chases across the lawn. Let a hawk appear, as occasionally one did, and all ameivas scattered immediately into adjacent hedges.

When we heard reports of lizard viruses from Brazil, it seemed to us that we must expand our efforts in that department. Previously we had processed only the occasional lizard that dropped into our laps, so to speak. Brazilian workers had recovered their viruses by dint of processing thousands of specimens, the rate of isolation being considerably under one per cent. How can you put your hands on such large numbers of these swift creatures unless they *are* in your lap? We learned that this had been accomplished by catching them with fine nylon nooses at the ends of poles. *Ergo,* that would be our technique, too.

Elisha was put in charge of a stepped-up lizard program, and Mohan was currently relieved of other duties to assist him. The main difficulty they experienced was that lizards didn't *want* the noose to be slipped around their necks. Oh, they caught some, all right, but these could be counted more truthfully by half dozens than by hundreds. I suspect that the Brazilian people were dealing with a fauna that included many more sluggish species than we had in Bush Bush. Indeed, I knew of only one kind in our forest (excluding latrine geckoes) that could be called slow. It was a small creature with a bulbous head and mottled body matching fallen leaves. You could almost pick them up by hand, but you did not see them every day.

TEGU LIZARD

Having noted that both mattes and jungle runners would enter Hav-a-hart traps baited for mammals, we tried to exploit that source. Tallies remained at the half-dozen level. I then decided to build a different sort of trap, on a pilot basis. If it were successful, our men could make others. This device was directed at an entirely novel kind of lizard, an arboreal species with rough scales that could often be seen ascending and descending forest trees. My trap was designed to encircle a trunk with a series of chambers that could be entered both from above and below and would lead in either case to an escape-proof compartment. Such a trap might catch snakes and tree frogs as well.

I spent weeks cutting half-inch hardware cloth into patterns that would fit this awkward configuration, sewing oddly shaped pieces together with wire and gradually nailing sections to a tree that I had chosen for the initial trial. I called my invention a "Trinidad and Tobago Tree-Trunk Traffic Trap," or "T. & T.T.T.T.T." for short. Leon could never get used to the number of T's, but to be sure not to leave any out he always referred to it as my "T.T.T.T.T.T.T.T.-T.T.T. etc." P.S.: it did not work.

One does not often have a chance to observe changes in animal distribution at the time of their occurrence. However, I am sure that we witnessed the invasion of Bush Bush Island by a small beach lizard from the nearby coast, and Tommy agrees with me. Prior to our establishment of two clearings, first at Moon's camp and later at We House, the continuous forest would have been inhospitable to creatures of open dunes. Even after we had cut trees widely enough to protect structures from falling branches, thereby creating fairly extensive "yards," the ground presented a "jungly" character, containing residual humus. But the combined forces of gardening and seasonal deluges eventually washed the substrate down to its essential element: sand.

The wonder is that these little striped lizards ever discovered those two insignificant forest openings. How was it possible for them to traverse a mile of swampland to get there? They could not have sensed that two artificial but suitable habitats had been created for them. I doubt very much that they came in as derelicts in our boats, either, despite the volume of boat-line traffic, for we maintained no gangplanks for them to climb aboard or debark. Somehow they must have made it on their own. This can then be regarded as an example of the pressures that constantly drive populations of animals beyond fringes of their normal ranges. If such forces operate in all directions, countless other striped beach lizards must have perished on fruitless expeditions that failed to end at sandy havens.

The ones that now adopted our doorsteps seemed carefree enough about the whole thing, as if Bush Bush were the most natural place in the world for them to live. They ran about, catching small flying insects that alit on bare ground in front of the gallery. I was puzzled by the fact that they seemed to be shedding their skins all the time— a need that I thought was only periodic. Also, it was always their heads and necks that looked ragged. Finally I got a good close-up view of one of them through binoculars and discovered that the lizard was not shedding at all: after each step it waved a front foot so rapidly as to form a blur, which I had mistaken for a tatter. I have not been able to interpret this action, but it may have something to do with hunting. Perhaps an insect thinks itself approached not by a rapacious saurian but only by another fluttering insect (though that could pose an equivalent danger in many cases).

Of course We House and Moon's camp will eventually be abandoned by TRVL. I wonder whether descendants of *Cnemidophorus lemniscatus* will find a way back to coastal dunes as forest margins reclaim lost territories?

We often longed to include caymans in our general reptile program. These giants are not lizards in the technical sense, despite a superficial resemblance. Instead, they are classified among crocodilians, which at once sends shivers up everyone's back. Our surveys of viruses in the Bush Bush fauna had covered almost all the common species of trappable mammal, bird and reptile except caymans. That hole urgently needed plugging, especially because caymans are swamp dwellers and must therefore be particularly often bitten by mosquitoes. But volunteers were scarce when we proposed this topic.

I heard legends, as well as authentic tales, about the size and menace of these beasts. One of our mosquito catchers had had the sole of a rubber boot torn from his foot by a large cayman in early days of TRVL—*he* wanted no part of the new project. During the time of year when Cascadoux fishermen were active in the swamp, I walked to the tip of Bush Bush Peninsula one day and surprised a number of gorged corbeaux that flopped heavily to overhanging trees. A terrible stench led me to the carcass of a cayman that fishermen had shot: it was well over six feet long and must have weighed at least a hundred and fifty pounds before corbeaux began their feast. But the jaws! That head could have engulfed my head and snapped it from its lissom cervical stem. On another occasion we all made a trek to Bois Neuf, west of Bush Bush Island, during the dry season, sometimes walking along broad, depressed trails in the marsh grass that James said were regular paths made and used by caymans. That day he carried a gun with our complete approval.

In this land where most country people are hunters, one might wonder why caymans remain undecimated. Answer: no commercial value. It is a cayman's good fortune to possess a hide that can be tanned only by a process that leads also to its virtual disintegration. The Latin name, *Caiman sclerops*, refers to a sclerotic plaque within each scale, a calcified center that must be dissolved out chemically before leather becomes pliable. By that time the skin, too, has reached a friable state approaching liquefaction. Therefore caymans have escaped "alligator" purse and shoe markets that would otherwise surely have been their destiny.

A remark by Moon Jury caused a complete turnabout in our pessimism regarding cayman studies. I guess this was a bit more than a mere "remark," since it had all sorts of exclamation points behind it. He had been removing mosquitoes from a trap near the margin of Petit Bush Bush Swamp when he was suddenly "rushed" by a cayman that chased him all the way back to camp.

"*All* the way?" I asked.

"I don' know, Doctor," he admitted. "*I* run all de way, an' I don' look back to see!"

That behavior in a cayman, he said, indicated a female building a nest. He had gone back cautiously and found a mass of vegetation that had been built up several feet above ground level and some six feet in width. The female was absent that time, but he predicted that she would return in a few days to lay eggs and would then remain to protect them until the young had hatched.

We enjoyed several good coffee klatches at the lab over this project. It was decided that baby caymans were exactly what we needed, for they could be handled even more easily than mattes and we could dispose them in traps about the forest and in the swamp at our pleasure, to discover what mosquitoes they attracted and what virus infections they acquired. But of course we would have to house and feed them as well.

James and Moon were put on cayman duty, to ascertain when the precious eggs were finally deposited. Once this major event occurred, the female was to be shot and James and his field crew would be assigned to erecting a wire enclosure about the mound, to prevent future babies from escaping. Meanwhile the men would construct another shelter for receiving hatchlings. This was a large cage, half in and half out of the water, at the beginning of our ramp across Petit Bush Bush Swamp, that would permit young caymans to take their choice between aquatic and terrestrial environments. In addition we placed attractive board floats in the pool compartment. We did not know what preferences they might have in early life, so it seemed best to give them both worlds. Mohan, when time decreed the need, would become babysitter and chief minnow catcher for the nursery.

Perhaps we were asking too much of James and Moon. How could they have been experts on cayman midwifery? At last they said that they *believed* the female had laid her eggs. Forthwith James shot her and said that next day he would surround the nest with protective wire. During that very night the mound was raided by a predator. Caymans do well to guard their incubators! Moon as usual postulated a matte as the marauder, though I doubted him anew because of mattes' diurnal habits.

We were saved from this fiasco by a second cayman that shortly plowed up a new mound near the first one. That was almost too good to have been hoped for. But like the unsuccessful T. & T.-

T.T.T., the scheme didn't work. This time the nest was duly enclosed and twenty-six babies clambered from the rotting pile two months later. We transferred them to their aquatic-terrestrial play-pen, and Mohan caught buckets of minnows to feed them. They refused to eat and, although a few of the babies lingered on for more than two months, all finally died. I wonder if they needed a mother?

Chapter 22

SWIFTS

I have a special fondness for swifts. This feeling began when I was quite a small boy in Coatesville and climbed to the roof of our stable, via a large cherry tree, to peer down the chimney at a saucerlike nest glued to the bricks a couple of yards below. Later I became interestetd in banding Chimney Swifts at Swarthmore College. For a while, one swift that returned to the same chimney each year held the longevity record for its species—nine years—in the Biological Survey's files in Washington.

We have only one kind of swift in Pennsylvania. Hence I was delighted to learn that at least eight species could be seen in Trinidad. Another one—the Large Black Swift—is listed for the island, but the record is not supported by museum specimens. Anyhow, eight is aplenty for a Pennsylvanian.

Perhaps one of the most remarkable (for they are all outstanding) in this group is the Cayenne Swift, a small, pied black-and-white gem. It is peculiar that in bird watching, or I suppose in any other avocation, the laws of chance operate in a fashion that results in an occasional person's total failure to come upon a find that is relatively common: say, the prospector who easily discovers copper ore but cannot stumble on quartz. The Cayenne Swift is not common, but neither is it particularly rare. During my first three years in Trinidad

I saw several of its nests, all seeming to be deserted, but never a bird.

Finally Tommy told me of a nest that he had discovered in Port-of-Spain's Botanical Garden, only half-a-mile from where I lived. Following his directions early one morning, I found it at once. The nest was, of all places, on the underside of the main forking branch of a devil's-ear tree. By the time I arrived, daylight was already intense, bats having long since retired. Still, I thought, there was a possibility that the swifts might be about, particularly if they had young ones to feed. Ants were foraging on droppings under the nest. An exposed root of the devil's-ear was conveniently located just where it could catch whatever fell from the dwelling. I should really change the term "droppings" to "castings," which refers to the regurgitated undigestible remains of flying insects that swifts commonly eject as a sort of cud.

Fresh droppings—castings—whatnot, these were spoor indicating occupancy of the nest, whether as a nursery or dormitory. Obviously one must come back at sundown to see a bird coming to bed, for no swifts were in evidence now. I asked a park guard about the nest —whether he had seen birds entering it recently or long ago—and to both questions he answered affirmatively. According to logic this could be a correct response, but it did not contain the exact information I wanted because he would have said "yes" to anything.

The nests of all swifts are remarkable for the use of saliva that goes into their construction. In these birds the salivary glands secrete excessive quantities of mucin at the time of nest building, and this substance serves to cement the components of a nest together and the nest itself to a vertical support—tree, cliff, chimney or cave wall. Edible-nest Swiftlets use relatively little nesting material and correspondingly more saliva, so that the extraction of soup stock is not much of a chore. Among the crested swifts of Asia, at least one species is known that omits nesting materials altogether and simply glues the egg itself to a branch.

Cayenne Swifts' nests would be an unprofitable source of soup. This species uses a large amount of soft plant material, which it first plasters against the trunk of a tree or, occasionally, the wall of a

CAYENNE SWIFTS

house. That seems to be the most important part of the salivary function, for to this base it now cements a long, downward-hanging tube of downy fibers, requiring a minimum of saliva. It has to enter the nest from below, making a bull's-eye approach to the tube. It then climbs up to a cupped shelf, near the top of the cylinder, which holds the eggs.

I was able to examine the castings at the foot of the tree by reversing my binoculars and using them as a magnifying lens. Sure enough, I could recognize fragments of insect exoskeletons. One would think these parts must soon be scattered by the wind, if not carried away by ants. That hypothesis was confirmed in the evening when I returned to the gardens shortly before six o'clock. The exposed root below the nest was as clean as if it had been washed. Therefore the droppings must have been deposited during the previous night or early in the morning before I had arrived. The lack of further day-time accumulation argued for the absence of young birds: the nest was occupied either by an incubating parent or by a nightly sleeper.

I had brought along a thermos flask containing some rum and water, so I now found myself a comfortable spot nearby where I could sit and lean against a tree trunk. Cup in hand, binoculars at the ready, I settled down to what must surely be my first glimpse of a homing Cayenne Swift. But not so! A guard (not the one I had met in the morning) suddenly appeared with the information that six o'clock was closing time and the command that I must get out. In vain I told him that I wanted only to sit quietly for an hour to see a bird enter its nest: he replied that I could come as early as I chose next morning and *see it go out*.

Foolishly I forgot to set the alarm, and when I awoke the sun was almost up. Nevertheless I drove to the gardens to check the castings hypothesis. Once more the root was spattered and ants had returned to clean the premises. No swifts were visible. As I was leaving I saw a public notice at the entrance gate. I had never read it, but for some idle reason I now did so. The first thing I saw was that "the Gardens shall be open daily until half an hour after sundown." I was sure I had been kicked out yesterday long before that. I rushed home to consult the newspaper. Sunset had been at 6:17 P.M., so a half hour later would be 6:47 P.M.

I had tried to persuade the evening guard that I was an Official Person, since our laboratory operates as part of the University of the West Indies, which receives support from the government of Trinidad and Tobago. He, quite properly, asked to see what credentials I had to substantiate a claim to Importance, but all I could do was brandish my binoculars and he was not impressed. All right, now I had credentials of a different sort!

That evening I took along not only binoculars and thermos flask but also the plainly dated *Trinidad Guardian* that clearly announced impending sunset at 6:17 P.M. In addition, I had checked the setting of my watch by the latest radio proclamation. Swifts are often slow about going to bed, but I felt that a 6:47 deadline should give me at least an even chance of success. But swifts aside, I now had a game to play with the guard.

Like Scrooge on the day after Christmas, I made sure that I would be on hand ahead of time. I needn't have bothered. When I reached the park at 5:40 P.M., it was swarming with Easter Monday strollers, shouting, laughing, playing guitars, littering the ground with paper and in general acting in a happy, uncontrolled way. No guards were in sight, or else they were lost in the crowd.

At 5:45 I saw my first bat. Soon many were flying, and my head turned this way and that as I thought each one might be a swift. Six o'clock came and went, and still the holiday throng milled about the walks and lawns with no sign of going home. Before long I could see the nest only as a silhouette against the darkening sky. Now people began to leave. The moment of 6:47 arrived with almost no remaining light, with few people, no guards and—worse—not a swift. I gave it up, for if I now thought I had seen a shadow shoot into the tube, I could not have been sure.

Next morning I reached my comfortable tree trunk at quarter to six. A fresh dropping was on the exposed root. Bats were flying. A guard—my first one—soon found me but expressed nothing other than mild amusement. At exactly 5:53 *two* swifts dropped out of the tube. I could not follow them against the dark background of the lawn, and when I ran into the open so that I could see the sky unobstructed by devil's-ear branches, they were not in view. Anyhow, I had seen them. I tried to exult as much as I thought the occasion deserved, but in spite of the triumph, an eight-minute vigil seemed too short. I should have had more trouble.

Other spectacular swifts to be found in Trinidad are the great Cloud Swifts that occasionally fly over from Venezuela and our little Fork-tailed Palm Swifts that live permanently on the island. I had no experiences with these beyond seeing them frequently. After such gratifying sights one might think that the four drab species of genus *Chaetura,* to which Chimney Swifts belong, would be anti-climactic. But since I bled and banded all of them, I actually hold this quartet in higher regard than their flashy cousins.

Swifts seen flying over Port-of-Spain and the adjacent open countryside are almost all Short-tails. To see Spine-tails, Lawrence's, and the rare Chapman's, you are better off in the Northern Range, and the higher the better. These birds are very difficult to tell apart in flight. All have sooty plumage, are roughly the same size, and vary principally in markings of the rump, which obviously must be out of sight when swifts fly overhead. On some ridges in the mountains one can look *down* on them. Then, if one is lucky, he may distinguish the sharply marked whitish rump-band of a Spine-tail, as opposed to more vaguely defined bands of other species. In any case, a bird in the hand is worth twenty of these creatures in the sky if one seeks to identify them.

Charlie Collins found a couple of species of these swifts nesting in abandoned concrete shafts that had been sunk into the ground on the old U.S. Air Force Base at Waller Field in connection with a drainage system. The birds used these retreats for both roosting and nesting, and Charlie learned to catch them by placing bird nets in a position that would intercept them as they fluttered out. In addition he used to stake nets along the highest ridge of the Arima Valley, where swifts, traversing the pass, often flew practically at ground level. To his great satisfaction and the furtherance of his studies, he succeeded in catching a few of the little-known Chapman's Swift on this ridge. His documentation of measurements, weights and molting sequences added fundamentally to scientific knowledge of that species.

Swifts had never entered my mind in relation to the Bush Bush program—at least not *Chaetura* swifts. I often saw them (unidentifiable, of course) soaring above the We House clearing, but they were far beyond reach of the canopy net. Yet these would have been extraordinarily interesting birds to bleed, because of their wide-ranging flight. Almost all other Bush Bush Forest birds lived permanently in that confine—at least we had no evidence that they plied across the swamp to the mainland. One never saw Golden-headed

Manakins, for example, flying over the savanna in either direction.

Most birds, then, contended with whatever viruses were already in the forest, and it might be a sad day when a new pathogen found its way to that isolated Eden. Should a viremic swift unaccountably drop from the skies over Bush Bush and be mosquito-bitten before its demise, it could serve as an agent for such an exotic introduction.

Speculation is a fascinating pastime. I would not have thought of swifts dropping from the skies, had we not found a freshly dead Leach's Petrel the day we hiked to Bois Neuf. This strictly marine bird was an even more unlikely windfall. Thus you have to keep the bizarre in mind: those things *do* happen.

Evidently I had prejudged *Chaetura*. Not many days after the canopy net had been lofted, Moon came to We House to report on something or other. As we were talking, he interrupted himself to say, "You got a rainbird, Doc!" I could see nothing, but at the far end, where the net had bunched up in the breeze, he could not only make out an avian form but identify it. Well, all swifts were "rainbirds" to these people, but that was a marvelous example of visual acuity. After Leon and I had lowered the net, I removed a common Short-tailed Swift, the first one I had held in Trinidad. I chalked up this day as one that was not likely to be duplicated.

"Why do you call them 'rainbirds'?" I asked.

"Because dey come wid rain—else you don' see dem," replied Moon.

It *was* raining that day, in fact. But his answer gave me another insight into the way bucolic inhabitants look at wildlife: they are aware of anything that is within their reach, because it might be both attainable and—better—edible. The empyrean holds no interest for them; they are oblivious to the gyrations of high-flying swifts on clear days. Only let the clouds close in near the earth, and previously nonexistent swifts seem magically to materialize from them.

Rain had already been my friend—I love downpours and dripping forest trees. Now I gave it extra thanks, for perhaps it would put more swifts into my hands. Formerly I had always told Motilal to take down, or at least fold, the nets when drops began to fall, for some small birds quickly become sodden and chilled during even

short showers. Now, however, I began to gauge the type of inunda-
tion we were about to receive. If it was presaged by lowering clouds
or, at the best, by swirling fog sifting through the jungle and touching
grass tips in Petit Bush Bush Swamp, I kept the nets spread and put
Motilal on extra-sharp watch along the ramp, regardless of the
soakings he received.

We caught one or two additional rainbirds in the canopy net, but
new strategy yielded about *twenty* from ramp nets. Now I had to
study each one critically—bird in one fist and book in the other—
for not all of these were Short-tails. In due course, over a period of
weeks, I ticked off Lawrence's and the Spine-tail. Then came a day
when Motilal brought in a handful of filled sacks and I could make
nothing of bird after bird but the impossible Chapman's. How could
a rare swift from summits of the Northern Range invade bird nets
in a swamp at sea-level—in numbers? I did not believe my own
diagnosis; perhaps my interpretation of the text was wrong. Less
likely, perhaps the book was faulty in its description. Whatever the
truth, I felt it mandatory to "sacrifice" one specimen, if only to vali-
date identity of the others. Our TRVL collection was understandably
void of skins of such a scarce bird. Thus I had no standards for
comparison there. But fortunately Charlie was still at Simla: he
alone in Trinidad could corroborate or correct my belief.

"Something very strange has happened to Chapman's Swifts this
year," he said. "They are supposed to be rare, but suddenly they
are turning up all over the place. I used to get them only at the pass
on Blanchisseuse Road—and only one or two, at that. Now I can net
them at Waller Field, and here you have taken an entire small flock
in Bush Bush. I don't know what's going on."

If he didn't know, neither did I. Though I caught more rainbirds
after that, Chapman's Swift was no longer among them.

Motilal and Moon were now indoctrinated by my interest in rainbirds. However, that did not motivate them to inform me of something I would like to have known weeks previously. After our "Chapman's" episode, Motilal returned to the paternal camp and reported
events of the day.

"Did you tell Doc 'bout de rainbirds in de moriche palm?" Moon asked.

"I don' know 'bout dem," said Motilal.

Thus I had been in ignorance for goodness knows how long of something that might prove to be important. Various hearsay reports began to trickle in. Unfortunately Moon was called away because of an accident in his family, but I tried to piece together what he had told Motilal and what Mohan claimed to have observed at first hand. Nothing really fit. Moon was supposed to have seen swifts by the hundreds entering a hole on one side of a palm for the night. Mohan stated that the birds did not sleep there but would take shelter in the tree during heavy rains. Two fundamental truths stood out: swifts were congregating in a hollow tree, and everyone was in agreement as to exactly which tree it was.

Of course information about the palm—its location, condition, height, etc.—included further garbled versions. Mohan's statement that he would not attempt to climb it because, "It is rot, Doc," was surely informative. But best of all, it was said by everyone to stand right alongside the boat line. "We'll stop for a good look on our way out tomorrow," I proclaimed.

The morning was both windy and rainy, a perfect setting for demonstration of Mohan's version of rainbirds' use of the hollow. As the boat took us away from camp, through the moriche swamp forest, I kept looking for likely roosting trees. But it was not until we had entirely cleared the forest margin that Mohan pointed ahead at a lone palm trunk. This was a topless bole that must have been dead for several years. Only about thirty feet tall, the tree was probably killed by a savanna grass fire in a bygone dry season.

"Look!" shouted Mohan. "One go in now." A swift came plummeting down, hovered for a moment, and disappeared. Mohan cut the motor and we drifted to the base of the trunk. A large, black termites' nest affixed just above ground level might help explain the stub's hollowness. Otherwise everything seemed as satisfactory as possible to me: the tree could not be more accessible, it was not very tall, and no other palms stood about to interfere with nets.

"Fine," I said. "I'll make a plan. Let's go." The instant Mohan re-started the outboard, a flock of swifts came boiling out of the en-trance—at the top, rather than the side, but at one side of the top! I believe there were about thirty, not hundreds, but that would be a substantial and gratifying number on any trapping day. They were all species of *Chaetura,* but I could not tell whether or not they were of one species.

I was now ready to piece information together by sifting all re-ports. If thirty swifts would resort to a stump in daytime (it was 11:30 A.M.) to avoid a shower, I wouldn't be astonished to see "hundreds" flock to that shelter at night. That sight would jibe with spectacles of Chimney Swift behavior such as I had observed in Pennsylvania on many a twilight evening.

Already I was scheming in several sneaky ways. Ideally one would want a sort of huge butterfly net to catch an entire emerging flock, but that meant designing and constructing such an artifice, and it might not work anyhow. Less efficient, but effective for our purposes if hundreds of swifts were really present, would be an ordinary bird net, on long bamboo poles, placed in front of the entrance-exit. The questions were: should the net be operated in the evening, to inter-cept incoming birds, or should it be put up after dark, to engage departing swifts in the morning? Before answering such queries, I wanted to observe flight patterns at both times. But now I was off to Surinam on another project.

It had to be several weeks later, therefore, before we got down to "Operation Rainbird." By this time I had become impatient and decided to strike at once, without preliminary studies of the birds' flight routines. As long as they slept in the hollow, all we had to do was reach our stations and raise the net before daybreak. On the first available afternoon, therefore, Moon, Motilal, Leon and I gathered equipment together, chief among which were two extraordinarily long poles that Motilal had cut in the forest, but including also two shorter, lighter poles that could be wired to the long ones if addi-tional height were needed. As Moon steered the boat along the winding channel through the swamp forest, with two long ends protruding from the bow, he remarked, "If I do dis all de way, I pass me driving test."

I was particularly eager to make all our preparations at the palm trunk long before any swift had thoughts of coming in for the night. To keep the environment as natural as could be, I proposed to leave only the poles, hidden in the grass so that they could not be mistaken for snakes. What I needed chiefly to know was how far a man would sink in the swamp, for his effective raising of a pole would be diminished in direct relation to the distance he sank in mud.

"You wet you foot, Doc!" shouted Moon as I sprang out of the boat. Indeed I did, above the knee, for how otherwise could I issue intelligent direction to a crew that must also maneuver in this medium?

Sweepstakes, of a kind, ensued. Dries was the only one offering negative opinions, though his comments were meant to needle rather than discourage. "The vulture saw you through a hole you didn't know about. What makes you think that swifts won't beat you, too?" Granted: total failure was possible. But this time Moon was fully on my side. When the vulture was at stake, he altered my trapping plans at the last minute and caught the bird. All credit to him, though I still feel that my net would have worked after the vulture's peephole was occluded.

But now Moon, Motilal, Leon and I all considered tomorrow's plan infallible. I tried to get some negative bets going, just for fun, but everyone favored the same horse. We would look like Fools of the Year if swifts escaped.

Everything was rehearsed in advance. The net must be stretched loosely in both dimensions, end loops close enough together so that deep pockets would form in the four horizontal panels and poles approximated to keep the whole structure slack. Birds, entering without speed, should find themselves in such lax trammels as to be unable to gain firm purchase anywhere.

The entire operation would not take much more than a minute, if all went well beforehand. But something else had to be considered. Birds bunching together in a net would become entangled only in the first layer. Later entrants could disengage themselves from backs

of their companions and fly away after a barely noted delay. I arranged the procedure so that my floundering team—with Moon on
one side of the boat line and Motilal on the other—would move the
net so that it passed slowly before the palm trunk during that
critical minute.

As usual I slept badly. At 4:30 A.M. the alarm went off and I had
some canned pears and coffee. Leon and I donned head lamps and
walked to Moon's camp. It was still too early to set forth. Now a
wind sprang up from the east and soft rain began to fall. We sat
about in a peculiar sleepy-eager state for a while. Then the horizon
vouchsafed a faintly glowing line. We piled into the boat. Moon
now wore the head lamp, running the motor and steering from the
stern, having to detect turnings of the channel through the black
moriche swamp forest by looking to right and left of our three
looming backs. Whether or not he had "passed his driving test" the
day before, he did so now. After all, he knew this watery corridor so
well that he might have guided the boat without prelude of dawn.

Once in the open, we found light increasing abruptly, though one
still would have to wait fifteen minutes to read newsprint. This, then,
was our quarter hour of grace, and we had a job that should not take
more than ten minutes. Moon cut the motor when we were still some
distance away, and we drifted silently to the palm trunk. I was over
the side, up to mid-thigh, in a jiffy. "You wet you foot, Doc!" Moon's
words echoed in memory, but now everyone remained ludicrously
mute. The amount of splashing going on would announce our presence to the most stupid of wild creatures. Perhaps a human voice
would be reassuring, an indication that mere men rather than caymans were surrounding the trunk!

Motilal and I strung one end of the net to a pole, on the palm-tree
side of the boat line, tying end loops with twine so that they could
not slide together and collapse the snare. Leon stayed in the boat,
which just about spanned the channel, and we used him as a middle-
man to get the other end of the net across to Moon. Then I waded
over and helped with similar arrangements on the second pole.

At a signal, both men lifted the net—a feat requiring all the effort
they could produce, because the poles were both heavy and un-

wieldy. Just then another shower was heralded by a stiff rush of air, and the billowing net slipped over the tip of the palm stub. I had warned the men not to let this happen, though now I could not blame them for it. At any rate, the net was stuck.

All this time there had been no signs of swifts. I believe everyone of us had kept his eyes on the exit, no matter what else was demanded—I know I did. Ordained events might as well begin now, so I decided there was no need for further silence. "Pull!" I shouted. "Don't mind if the net gets torn—get it off the stub so that you can hold it several feet away!"

Finally it broke loose, taking a piece of trunk material with it. The men's tugging had caused the stub to wobble, and by now we were all talking loudly at once. Still no birds!

"I'm going to slap the tree," I said.

"Yes!" urged Moon, "now is de time!"

A stranger might then have witnessed a tableau beyond comprehension: the boat, crosswise of a channel . . . two men, deeply sunken in a swamp, striving to hold a filmy net aloft against gusts accompanying a downpour . . . a third man, streaming with muck, embracing the dead palm and striking it mightily with open hands. "Come on, swifts! Out! Out!"

Later Moon said he thought it was his fault. Though the birds had been entering the roost every night up to the last time he happened to observe them, he had not checked them on the evening before this occasion. Since I had already thought of that scouting maneuver but decided to omit it, my fault was greater than his.

I asked him to watch at dusk, just in case the swifts had simply spent a single night elsewhere. But the tree stub was ignored. It continued vacant thereafter.

Chapter 23

HUMMINGBIRDS

*I*f swifts were generally inaccessible to bird nets in Trinidad, their hummingbird relatives made up for such distant behavior by zooming in from all directions. Of the sixteen known species on the island, I finally saw thirteen, a sure indication that the other three are rare, since it was not only my eyes but the nets, as well, that collaborated in a four-year search for them.

Happily these little jewels were all but exempt from our bleeding program. That was not because we were "soft" on them, as Leslie might have insinuated, though we one and all admitted that they were about as lovely as birds can get. Our problem was to obtain any blood at all, whether or not the creatures died. Following either cardiac or jugular puncture, a high percentage of humming-birds succumbed, and we finally removed them from the agenda.

But they did not remove themselves. On any bird-netting morn-ing at Fort Read, in Vega de Oropouche or in Brazil Village, we had to spend part of our time extricating hummingbirds from net meshes. Sometimes they gave us more trouble than larger birds, owing to their lodging halfway through a mesh that could have engaged no more than a head or leg of a tanager. The tiniest species, indeed, often passed right on through, as if the net were no more than air.

Obviously our procedure should have been to release hummers as soon as we had freed them from nylon threads. But that reckons without Tommy's list-making compulsion. He instructed everyone to bag these birds exactly as all the others. At the field table they would then be carefully identified and sexed, appropriate data being entered into a register. Tommy still sits on all this information, and I have no idea what he intends to do with it. Secretly, I believe he simply wanted to regale himself with repeated holding of hummingbirds, a practice of which I never tired either.

A male Ruby-Topaz in the hand, for example, provides unsurpassable moments. Herklots dispassionately describes it thus:

> Entire crown, the feathers of which are somewhat erectile, in reflected light brilliant ruby-red. Chin, throat and upper breast in reflected light brilliant golden-yellow. Hind neck and upper back velvety black; rest of upper parts dark bronze-olive. The tail bright chestnut faintly glossed with purple and tipped with dark bronze-olive. Wing flight-quills dusky, faintly glossed violet. Underparts grayish-brown or sepia; leg feathers white; under tail-coverts cinnamon-rufous.

Of course we caught many female and immature birds that put on no such show, but it was really somewhat marvelous that almost every time a camera-toting visitor went netting with us, a male Ruby-Topaz would beg to have its picture taken.

I fell into the same practice at Bush Bush. Following Tommy's example blindly, I requested Motilal to bring in all hummers so that I could record (and enjoy) them. That stood me in great stead one day when Motilal brought me a life lister! This was a Starthroat, considered very rare by Herklots, though I later saw two others along Andrews' Trace high in the Arima Valley.

Hummingbirds encountered in low jungle are most likely to be species of so-called Hermits, though they are not restricted to that habitat, and other sorts of hummers invade dark forests as well. But Hermits outnumber the rest of their tribe in such recesses. All three Trinidadian species were common around We House: Guy's, Longuemare's, and the Hairy Hermit. They were flower feeders without doubt, for I often saw them hovering in front of sticky *Heliconia* inflorescences, but in addition they gleaned tiny insects from foliage. If I have not accorded the cocorite palm its full complement of attendants, I can add at least one more in the shape of a Hairy Hermit that I observed as it made its hovering way up one frond after another, gathering morsels too small for me to see but obviously not wasting time.

Our scattered netting areas were not suitable for detailed studies of hummingbirds, whereas concentration on a small section of Bush Bush was ideal. In time I decided that the mere listing of captures of hummers at We House might be improved upon. I had been toe-clipping small forest mammals. Without bands small enough to mark Hermits, Emeralds and so on, why not then *feather* clip them? Blood or no blood, I should at least learn whether I was trapping a resident or a mobile population.

But would such mutilation impair their flight? After all, a hummingbird is almost all wing, when you get down to its essentials, and I would be loath to allow my curiosity to wreak tragedy on even one of them. I bolstered myself with reflections on the engineering "margin of safety" that is built into all forms of life, including ourselves, and decided that a single clipped feather would not matter.

According to the species, therefore, I began to snip a half inch from the outermost primary feather on the right side, then the next primary in a following bird, and so on until I had to begin on the left wing. Naturally the remaining stubs would be molted in time, but for the present I had a clue to individual identities, as good as if the hummers had been banded, and I looked forward to enlightenment.

Results of this study brought me into a conflict of opinions with Tommy and Elisha. I had already been vaguely aware that in our three bird-netting areas hummingbirds seemed to have become less abundant than when we first established those bleeding and banding centers. Yet we maintained a rate of about ten per cent of recaptures of other species. That was true in each locus, despite their being physically quite different: burned-over scrub at

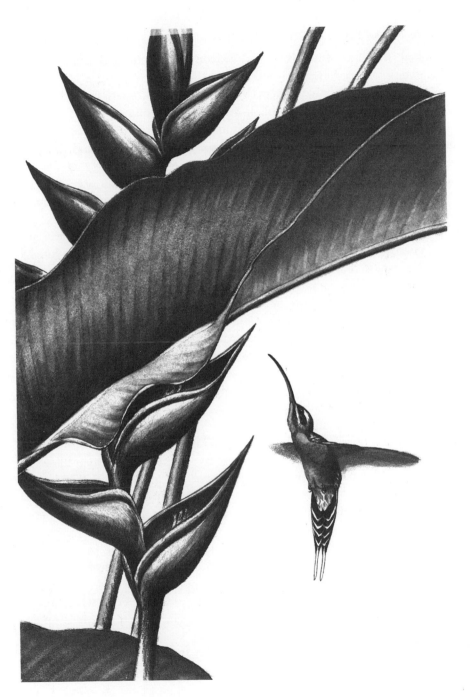

GUY'S HERMIT AND HELICONIA

Fort Read, a citrus grove in Vega de Oropouche and a neglected planting of cashew trees near Brazil Village.

Consider what happened to any netted bird, apart from the unexpected arrest of its flight. If it was not a hummer, it was placed in a sack, taken out and bled from the neck, re-sacked and passed to me, again removed to be banded, and finally released. Surely that must be an experience rendering a captive wary of being caught again. The nets were always erected at the same sites, so that even if the snare was hard to see, a bird might reasonably associate danger with the general area.

But hummingbirds received preferential treatment. There was no question of needles. In consequence they were scarcely manipulated. The worst that could happen to them was to be held in admiration for a few moments longer than necessary. Each time a male Black-throated Mango or Ruby-Topaz came to hand, one automatically turned it this way and that, to catch incident light just right for observation of its glinting brilliance.

Then away! We tossed the hummingbirds high, to prevent a second imprisonment in the net, and buzzing wings carried them off intact, unmolested and (one would think) without traumatic psychological experience.

Here is an example of the constant difficulty confronting students of animal behavior. How easy it is to interpret what we see in terms of our own substituted and imaginary reactions! The hypothesis I proposed, based on observations I have just related, was that hummingbirds are (for some unknown reason) smarter, more wary, or keener-eyed than larger birds—perhaps all three. But of these traits, "smartness" must be the key; otherwise, keen vision should have avoided the first net encounters and wariness might have recognized danger in the station wagon with its peculiar robots wielding sharp-needled syringes.

It is hazardous to propose gleamings of intelligence when birds are concerned, for the whole tribe is said to be highly stupid. Learning ability is present, but of low order. The most effective actions of birds are performed on the basis of splendid instincts.

Nevertheless I had another prop to my hypothesis. Each new

ground net set up in Bush Bush, as I expanded my program, initially caught more hummers than later on. And it was several months after I began to wing-clip them before a single idiot Hairy Hermit returned to a net. By that time I had marked thirty-six of these creatures, distributed among six species. Yet the We House clearing was still full of hummingbirds, traversing it like arrows or stopping to feed on heliconias a few feet from my swivel chair on the gallery. Many times their trajectories took them straight toward a net. Now, however, they stopped short of it, hovering in stationary contemplation. With their ability to fly up, down, sideways and backwards, they simply maneuvered until they topped the net and were then off like darts in their original directions. If they had learned about the nets in one lesson, weren't they "smarter" than other birds? Tommy and Elisha insisted I had no proof. Obviously if I couldn't catch them, I could not aver that they were wing-clipped. But how else explain the behavorial change?

Much though I enjoyed Trinidad's wealth of hummingbirds, I realized that only a few miles away in Venezuela there were scores of additional species. Therefore I hoarded several days of "local leave" in order to accompany Charlie Collins on a visit to a biological field station called Rancho Grande, situated in a mountain pass above Maracay, west of Caracas. Bird netting in the pass captured some hummers, while it was possible to observe others with binoculars. Though most of the species were unfamiliar to me, I was aided in identifying them by use of Rodolphe Meyer de Schauensee's new book, *Birds of Colombia,* as well as by examining bird skins in the small museum maintained at Rancho Grande.

I enjoyed looking through the cabinets to confirm some of the species that we had handled and others that flew nearby. One was a long-tailed hummingbird. We had netted two rather ordinary greenish hummers and examined them closely, but the long-tailed sort eluded capture. Its six-inch tail appeared to be about three times as long as the head and body. In the misty trees of the mountain pass the bird looked black, but that did not detract from the novelty of its proportions: it was exotic enough to please any naturalist. But when I lifted a specimen from its place in the museum tray, I was amazed to see that it was a brilliant green, violet and blue thing, the forked tail feathers shining especially vividly. Rodolphe calls it the "Blue-throated Sylph," while in Latin it is known as *Aglaiocercus kingi.* I wonder who Mr. King was, to have such a gem named after himself? The greenish hummers we had caught now proved to be females of the species.

Mr. Leadbeater is another honored fellow, for a bird netted one morning was a male Violet-fronted Brilliant, a hummer with glittering violet crown and shining emerald underparts, *Heliodoxa leadbeateri.* Its proportions were normal, but the colors again seemed extravagant within the gloom of clouds and forest.

Whether or not these sheens and glints are for the admiration of females (a topic too controversial to pursue), they *are* paraded before that audience. In bright weather, especially on sunny mornings, many males of gaudily adorned hummingbird species perform display flights in front of perched females. Hovering, darting, dipping, turning, sometimes describing pendulumlike motions, they present every angle of their several iridescent patches to incident light, reflections presumably producing an overpowering dazzle.

Some tropical hummingbirds, especially the various Hermits, are largely earth-brown or dull bronze in color. A display flight by males would seem ludicrous, for their plumage is no different from females'. In this case males are sensible: they sit on specially selected twigs and appear to sing. The result sounds to us like twitters and squeaks, but it serves to notify the forest that males are available. Both tribes—the garish and the drab—flourish. What we must fear and abhor are anthropomorphic interpretations of how they manage to do it.

Until recently there were no standardly accepted English names for tropical American birds. Among hummers, a few group titles such as Hermit and Mango were readily understood by ornithologists, but they would still preferably talk about *Phaethornis* or *Anthracothorax.* Eugene Eisenmann, of the Linnaean Society at the American Museum of Natural History in New York, put a stop to such nonsense in his pamphlet, "The Species of Middle American Birds." In this classic he made a plea that his proposed vernacular terminology, which was the result of wide consultation among experts in addition to his own opinions, be accepted by one and all. Now Rodolphe had extended that practice in his *Birds of Colombia,* and I was enthralled by the enrichment of our language that has ensued. How could he give distinctive names to one hundred thirty-five species of Colombian hummingbirds without becoming prosaic? I discovered that he had used thirty-nine different group terms to refer to them.

The commonest one was, understandably, the basic word, "hummingbird." Twenty such birds were simply called this or that kind of hummer. Fourteen hermits constituted the next most abundant category. After that I found nine puff-legs, eight emeralds and six star-frontlets. Smaller groups, containing one to five members apiece, can be alphabetized thus: Avocet-bill, Barbthroat, Blossom-crown, Brilliant, Coquette, Coronet, Fairy, Goldenthroat, Helmet-crest, Hillstar, Inca, Jacobin, Jewel-front, Lancebill, Mango, Metal-tail, Plumeleteer, Sabrewing, Sapphire, Sapphire-wing, Sickle-bill, Starthroat, Sun-angel, Sunbeam, Sylph, Thorn-bill, Thorntail, Topaz, Train-bearer, Violet-breast, Violet-ear, Whitetip, Wood-nymph and Woodstar. Think what Shakespeare could have done with that list!

Despite the prevalence of hummingbirds in Bush Bush, I found only three nests during my years there. Of course I was not searching specifically for them, but it would have been gratifying to stumble on a few more. The first one belonged to a Common Emerald and was saddled precariously near the end of a thin, hanging branch of a tree at the tip of Bush Bush Peninsula where a dead cayman would later appear. When even mild breezes blew, this nest swayed violently. However, hummingbirds build their homes so deep that they must incubate with bills and tails held almost vertically, and there was little danger of eggs' tumbling out even when stronger winds swept in from the east. If this nest was relatively secure from the elements, it must have been a total refuge from predators: in the first place they would not be likely to espy it, and after that it would be a hazardous journey to crawl or clamber down that slim branch.

Nests of hummers fall into two types: the "saddle" configuration, in which building materials are felted together upon a foundation, and "hanging" ones that somehow can be fastened to tips of downward-arching leaves such as palms, bananas and heliconias. My next nest was of the second sort. I found this one only after I had cut it down while clearing a trail near We House. As I swung the cutlass to right and left, vines, fronds and saplings collapsed before it. A young cocorite palm, not yet having a trunk, presented an obstruction, so down it came along with everything else.

To my dismay I now saw that one of its leaf tips bore a nest, obviously belonging to one of the hermits, which fall in the "hanging" class. The cup was empty, and after searching the ground unsuccessfully for broken eggs or dislodged young, I concluded with relief that its mission had already been accomplished. Besides, no parent was flying about anxiously. This was a trophy too precious to abandon, so I cut off the leaf tip with its dependent burden and tacked it to the wall inside We House, where it edified visitors for years.

In time the leaf deteriorated, and the nest did too, until the display lost its attractiveness. When I decided to clean house one day, the hermit's nest presented me with an opportunity previously denied. Now I could take it apart to see how it had been fabricated. At the bottom, carefully covered over, I found two desiccated eggs! Apparently my blundering approach with the cutlass had been a signal for the mother not only to go into hiding but first to rearrange nesting materials to conceal her treasures—perhaps also to retain warmth.

The last nest I hate even more to talk about. This one belonged to Longuemare's, the smallest of our hermits. I found it at the tip of a low palm leaf overarching a trail north of We House in such a position that anyone walking past would surely jostle against it. Two uncovered eggs were present. I had recently been plaguing James Thomas with requests to clear that trail. I called that off at once and instead posted signs on either approach along the path with the warning: "Hummingbird nest across trace. Do not cut."

Alas for this nest, or alas for science! Charlie Collins immediately stated a need for the baby birds, should affairs progress successfully to that stage. One of the many aspects of evolutionary studies of birds involves knowledge of the presence or absence of natal down on hatchlings. Some birds have none, while in those that do possess it the distribution of tufts varies. Information concerning these diversified patterns assists interpretation of relationships among species, species groups, families, etc. Charlie already had the required specimens of Hairy Hermits but badly needed representatives of both Guy's and Longuemare's. Might he have these?

With outward cheerfulness I agreed. Inwardly I cursed myself for a weakling and a skunk.

Chapter 24

BUTTERFLIES AND BOYS

On my trip to Surinam I observed something foreign to everything I had ever imagined entomologically: a palm tree stripped
by caterpillars. Rather, there were many stripped palms, both within
towns and throughout the countryside, and I assumed caterpillars
had been responsible. Though I knew that practically every plant
and tree in the world has specific pests that chomp at its foliage,
I had falsely concluded that palms are so tough they were spared
such selective and appreciative feeders.

Tommy and I had immediately made the delightful acquaintance of Dr. Geijskes, Director of the museum in Paramaribo. When
I mentioned my amazement at defoliation of palms, that oracle
brought me a tray of pinned butterflies named *Brassolis sophorae,*
the culprits. They were rather large, with a wing expanse of about
three or three and a half inches, and the colors were subdued without being drab: generally dark brown but with dull orange bands
on the fore and hind wings. The Director handed me also a leaflet
on *Pests of Palms in Surinam* in which I was able to correct my
former misapprehension for all time.

The butterfly occurs from Surinam south into Brazil and beyond.
(Clearly I could never have seen it in Trinidad, Panama, or Mexico.)
Eggs are laid in masses averaging about two hundred. The larvae

remain gregarious through their seven pereiods of growth—interrupted by molts—that culminate in the formation of chrysalides.
Contrary to my prejudice, palm leaves cannot be extraordinarily
tough, for even newly hatched, first-stage caterpillars are able to
eat them. The developing army requires several months to complete
its feeding orgy. If a palm happens to be infested with many armies,
the tree will be stripped. Overinfestation will exhaust food supplies
before caterpillars have fully matured, and then everyone is in
trouble. The tree stands denuded while famished worms die. Severe
losses have been experienced in some of Surinam's rich coconut
plantations during certain seasons of caterpillar plagues. Luckily the
trees are not killed, but it may take a full year for them to restore
leafy crowns and resume bearing profitable crops.

The butterflies can be seen sometimes by day, but they are more
likely to fly at dusk and probably even at night, thus behaving more
like moths. No effective way of attacking them has been discovered.
The only combative measures recommended in the pamphlet were
centered on caterpillars, though admittedly spraying a palm crown
with DDT is almost impossible when the tree is tall, the ground
below is uneven, and a strong breeze at foliage level wafts the
mist from its target.

After returning to Trinidad I consulted the few available books on
my shelf and in TRVL's library, in hopes of placing *Brassolis* in
some relationship to butterflies I already knew. With real astonishment I found in Essig's *College Entomology* that the somber creature is practically a kissing cousin of such glorious celebrities as
metallic morphos and spectacular owls. Then, in Kaye's *Catalogue
of the Butterflies of Trinidad,* I read that *Brassolis sophorae* had
been known on our island since 1894 and was considered to be "an
important pest of coconuts." How, then, had I missed noting its
depredations? On reflection, I could now remember having seen
palms with ragged leaves, but I had always ascribed such damage
to storms or some obscure blight. At least I had never observed total
defoliation as in Surinam.

Completely humbled, I began regarding palm trees as so much
spinach and almost at once discovered another feeder. Leon had

planted a coconut along with his plantains at We House about a year before. By this time it had developed its eighth or ninth leaf, as high as my head, though they still sprang like a jet from the ground without enough girth to form a trunk. On one frond I noticed signs of leaf gnawing. Only a brief search was needed to reveal a solitary skipper caterpillar, concealed between two parallel leaflets that it had drawn together with silk.

As hesperid caterpillars go, it conformed generally in its hairless body, thin neck and mobile head. However, it was more flattened than standard form, and the cuticle's remarkable transparency was another somewhat unusual feature, though I remember an even more glassy caterpillar in a heliconia leaf on the Volcan de Chiriqui in Panama. In both cases one could see superficial arborizations of the respiratory tracheae beneath the "skin," down to bifurcations at the limit of fine vision. The We House palm-eater came under my lens only because I had rudely torn its silken anchors apart. When one is so naked as to have no privacy even for internal organs, embarrassment must be intense. Within ten minutes the caterpillar had located the detached roof and tacked it down again.

Caterpillars should have abounded at We House, for jungle clearings permit weeds to grow profusely, and these in turn attract butterflies which then might be expected to lay eggs on suitable food plants in the vicinity. But caterpillars, like hummingbird nests, are hard to find. One such crawler, however, obligingly presented itself to me. As I was bleeding a bird on the gallery one day, I heard something drop to the ground near me. When I was able to shift my attention from the syringe, I beheld a large caterpillar moving across the yard. It was about three inches long and almost half an inch thick, light brown with some darker-brown longitudinal stripes. The tail ended in a short fleshy fork, while its head had a peculiar wedge-shaped contour. I had never seen anything like it but suspected it might be the larvae of a large noctuid moth that I had collected in the Arima Valley and seen at Piarco Airport.

But whence had this caterpillar dropped? Immediately above the spot where it landed was the edge of the roof, and beyond that a high overarching leaf of the cocorite palm. Was this another palm eater? When large caterpillars consume leaves, one can see the damage. More important, one can often find their conspicuous droppings. The cocorite leaf was intact and the ground (which Leon kept swept) was clean of frass. Therefore the crawler must have fallen from the roof.

To those not familiar with caterpillars, it may sound as if the investigation of this one was baffling. Not at all. Already the negative evidence began to have significance. Indeed the "plop" was the first clue, and the fact that I found the caterpillar rapidly moving from the site of its impact, rather than lying curled there, was a second indication of the truth.

All these circumstances and events strongly suggested that the caterpillar was full-fed and ready to pupate. It is characteristic of many lepidopterous larvae to become gypsies for a day or two before spinning cocoons, hanging up as chrysalides, burrowing underground, or doing whatever their individual instincts dictate. Such dispersal must be beneficial to each species in the long run, but surely many are lost at this time, either by getting into the wrong places (for they seem to travel wildly and blindly) or by drawing attention to themselves. As feeding "worms," they go to elaborate lengths to remain inconspicuous, but while wanderlust is upon them, predators don't have to seek.

Therefore I did not hesitate to put the creature in a jar without anything to eat (not that I would have known what kind of greens to proffer anyhow). Instead I added a few dry sticks in case it needed supports for spinning a cocoon. Since the caterpillar might be of an unusual kind, I gave it to Tommy at the lab. At first he could not name the species, though he was certain he had seen it before. Then he remembered that it was a *Caligo* larva.

At last everything fitted into place. *Caligo* is the genus of owl butterflies, common enough around We House. The caterpillars of one species, Tommy said, feed on leaves of the banana and heliconia. Leon's plantains being of the banana family, and wild heliconias growing almost to We House's doorstep, the caterpillar could have originated from any direction except above. In its compulsive safari, it simply arrived at the house, climbed, came to an edge and dropped.

Owl butterflies—with their great eye spots on the under surface of the hind wings—and metallic-blue morphos—called "emperors" in Trinidad—both frequent shady places such as cocoa plantations and forest interiors. At Bush Bush I was impressed by the fact that small groups of each species often seemed to remain in a chosen small area for days or even weeks at a time. Of course the Moon Jury clan had known that all their lives. On one occasion we had a visitor from Africa whose hobby was butterflies but whose allotted time in Trinidad was extremely short. He desperately wanted to catch both a caligo and a morpho, and this might be the only chance in his career. Mohan impressed this gentleman by conducting him to a thicket only a few steps away from camp where the lifetime ambition was at once consummated.

It was possible, of course, that these favored sites held shifting populations and that their constant occupancy was due to some kind of attraction that would lead every roving butterfly to perch here rather than anywhere at random. I tried to resolve that question by catching several morphos and owls, rubbing scales from a wing and sticking on a small numbered square of adhesive tape. (Wing clipping would not have been a reliable means of recognition, for many insects already had ragged margins.) Then I released them where they had been captured and asked everyone to keep watch, not only at the original spot but at all other known points of convergence. Unfortunately the tapes did not adhere well, though you could still discern the rubbed areas after they came off. My field staff gave me no reports—I doubt that they really bothered with that project, for there were many important things for them to do. The best I can say is that a couple of owls did linger for several days at the same focus, but I consider the experiment too slim for drawing conclusions.

OWL BUTTERFLY

Kaye's catalogue of Trinidadian butterflies had not helped me with anything but the palm-eating *Brassolis,* for it was a technical volume written for professional lepidopterists. If you knew already what your butterfly was, you could read about it here. Otherwise there was no means of tracking it to its proper species, so I went along for years without being able to put a name to an array of forms which I came to know well.

Finally Tommy unearthed a series of illustrated articles by Frank Ambard, privately published by Shell Trinidad in 1958–1959 in an advertising periodical conceived by the promotion department. Tommy had carefully collected the items and bound them in a manila folder.

Mr. Ambard stated that 597 species of Trinidadian butterflies have been recorded in official literature, but that he was aware of about twenty-five additional kinds in private collections. The chances are that many others remain to be "discovered." This is somewhat discouraging to a beginner, for it means that the butterfly probem is much more formidable than the avian, which presents only four hundred or so forms to the student. But the beauty of Ambard's account, from my standpoint, was that he discussed chiefly the commonest species. Naturally he yielded to an urge to include some rarities, but these were conspicuous, large ones. Thus the majority of the fauna—those butterflies that would occupy a specialist's time—were omitted, and I was ready to make a beginning.

The color illustrations were far from top-grade, but again I felt no cause for complaint. Almost a hundred butterflies were figured, each with a short paragraph of text telling something of distribution and habits of the corresponding insect. Unfortunately there was nothing on food plants of the respective caterpillars, though I could now use Kaye's catalogue as a cross reference to that subject.

Vernacular names were extremely stimulating, for they seemed to be entirely of local manufacture. Some were derived from French occupation of the island two centuries ago, e.g., "cravat" and "morbleu." English ones had no relation to usage elsewhere. A swallowtail, for example, was called a "page." The closest parallel I could find to North American terminology was in the case of the local Trinidadian buckeye, *Junonia geneviva*, known here as a "donkeyeye." This is undoubtedly an instance of "convergent" terminology, for the eyed wing pattern would inevitably suggest some such name to English-speaking bucolic populations.

But when it came to "Grecian flags" and "Italian shoemakers," I was at a loss to discern the evolution of language on even a local basis. These are names that have sprung up here *de novo* and have somehow become entrenched within a small community of butterfly collectors. However I was grateful for handles of any sort and determined to become adept at using them. My greatest satisfaction, after absorbing Ambard's articles, was to reach a long-delayed introduction to the commonest butterfly of all at the lab, a medium-sized red and black insect that swarmed both out of doors and inside our very offices. He called it the "coolie," *Amartia amalthea*.

The We House caterpillar having proved to be an ordinary caligo, Tommy took it home to his sons, Bruce and Brian, who were both butterfly enthusiasts, as all boys ought to be. Soon the larva formed a chrysalis, and a little more than ten days later it hatched. Naturally I had to see the butterfly. Immediately a mystery of long standing presented itself in familiar disarray. It would be impossible to make even a rough guess as to the numbers of cocoons of Cecropia, Polyphemus and Promethea moths I gathered not only as a youth but throughout adult life, as well: certainly many hundreds of them. As I became older and presumably wiser, I tried to keep the cocoons in as natural an environment as possible —that is, in attempted duplication of the settings where I had found them. They must by no means be brought into the house but should be exposed to wind and sun and rain and fluctuating outdoor temperatures.

Yet very few of the moths that emerged from these "captive" cocoons grew perfect wings. Rarely, one or more wings failed to expand at all. The usual result was that when they had finally "set" at full size, they nevertheless remained rumpled in varying degrees.

At the same time I had excellent evidence that truly "wild" cocoons produced perfect specimens, with wings as flat as if they had been pressed between glass plates. This phenomenon could not often be verified in the case of females, for one does not ordinarily encounter that sex. But the life history of these moths entails a waiting stage after hatching, during which females attract males by emitting an attracting scent. As soon as she is found by a male, her lure ceases, but if you place her in a screened cage inaccessible to males, eager husbands continue arriving until clouds of them (especially Prometheas) may flit about the enclosure. And all of them have classical geometrically flat wings.

The Aitkens' Caligo—poor thing—had such excessively warped

pennants that I doubt it ever could have flown. Unquestionably it did not have that opportunity, for I am sure it became part of the boys' butterfly collection. The sight of it reminded me of a compensation that partly detracts from the undesirability of crippled captives. Home-hatched specimens are the handsomest you will ever see in spite of crumpled wings. Not a scale has been lost in attempted flight, and the colors obtrude unbleached. This owl had wonderful "eyes," outlined in sharply contrasting concentric circles, while caligos in Bush Bush Forest often appear dull and heavy-lidded.

Bruce and Brian loved to come bird-netting with us, if it were not a school day, especially when we went to Brazil Village. This open region supported great numbers of butterflies. While we adults tended to our bleeding, banding and recording, the boys tired themselves out by running endlessly with *their* sort of net.

Nearby lived an East Indian family, headed by an individual to whom we referred (among ourselves) as One-Eye. We had sought his friendship when we first contemplated working at Brazil Village, because we needed someone to guard our chicken-baited mosquito traps that were set out on afternoons preceding bird-netting mornings. Unless a local person kept his eye on them, we would find that chickens had developed unprecedented powers of flight during the night—babies, at that! For his services, One-Eye was to receive the chickens after they had performed their entomological tasks. The arrangement appealed to him, and we never lost a bird or a trap.

These people seemed to have only one child, which is almost unheard of in Trinidad. Their little boy became a regular spectator of our strange doings. He was especially interested in the banding and releasing procedure, after surgery had been completed. As I was ready to let the birds go, he wanted to touch each one. I could not tell whether he was awed or enraptured, though it was probably the latter. He never spoke, and I thought he might be mute until I discovered that he would answer questions quite freely.

When Bruce and Brian arrived with butterfly nets one morning, this dark waif was transported beyond all definitions of joy. I could see the desire to use a net himself oozing from his pores, but he still maintained his excellent manners. Finally Bruce and Brian got tired and offered him a "turn," but he took off so violently after a sulphur butterfly that the net was in danger of being torn to pieces and Tommy quickly came to the rescue.

However, the child had caught the butterfly. Now the Aitken boys let it go, saying that sulphurs were "too common!" I suppose they were right. A butterfly collection should be variegated: what kind of display would a thousand specimens of the same kind make, unless they had been gathered for an artistic arrangement rather than a collection?

Henceforth I remained on the lookout not only for Bruce and Brian but also for myself. Usually I yielded captives to the boys, because I had insufficient time to tend to them. Shortly before Christmas one year, Motilal arrived at We House carrying the leaf of a pois doux sapling that enclosed a larva. "Dis one full of B's," he said. Indeed it was. As I pried the nest apart, without breaking its holding strands, I beheld a remarkable caterpillar that immediately proclaimed itslf another member of the Hesperiidae, or skipper butterflies. Its skin was white, its head a light tan, and the "B's" Motilal mentioned were spiracular markings down each side of the abdomen—finely etched lines, in the shape of squarish capital B's or blocklike figure eights, as if drawn by a sharp stylus with India ink.

What better Chrismas present for a pair of young lepidopterists? I delivered the caterpillar to Tommy with best wishes of the season. In due time, after New Year's, he deposited a net-covered box on my desk at the lab. "Here's your skipper," he said. "The boys don't collect them: they say they're too hard to identify; most of them look nearly alike."

Sulphurs are "too common" and skippers are "too hard."

How right that is! I feel exactly the same way about several aspects of life, though it had not occurred to me to express the sentiment as tellingly as Bruce and Brian did. How nice it might be if all butterflies had qualities like Mona Lisa and the Taj Mahal—

rare in the extreme but instantly to be recognized and worshiped.

In a way I approved of the dim future facing One-Eye's two-eyed, wide-eyed little boy. No one was likely ever to sponsor him: who, in the Trinidadian government, even knew that he existed, aside from a local rural schoolmaster? And how would that commander of the three R's, despite his best intentions, recognize something different in this child who wanted only to catch butterflies and touch birds? The teacher would never know, and the pupil would not realize, that he possessed an uncommon trait of which our world is much in need. Forever uninformed and forever untroubled by matters of terminology and all the other claptrap of advanced education, the boy, developing into a man, must therefore remain limited to that best of all preoccupations, which is to see and to admire.

Such a person is the only one who comes to know and feel the *real* Trinidad. He develops into a James Thomas or a Moon Jury and can translate the essence of every forest trail for you. You don't find that kind of information on picture postcards. The average tourist is likely to take a taxi from Port-of-Spain up the scenic Maraval Valley and then down to Maracas Bay on the North Coast, believing he is absorbing something that is Trinidad. Government clerks attend to tasks that keep the nation running and thus become convinced that *they* are Trinidad. But the real Trinidad existed even before Columbus first sighted the Trinity Hills on the southern coast, when the only indigenous primates were howler and cebus monkeys and a few savage hominids. Though not much of this remains, the fragments are there to delight perceptive eyes and souls.

What would you like to hear or see that I have not mentioned? You need only to get out of the taxi, anywhere along the road, and begin walking—or better yet, just stand still.

Glossary

Ampullaria.—A genus of large fresh water snail. In the southern United States, one species is fed upon exclusively by Everglade Kites.

Antibody.—A substance manufactured by the body in response to invasion by bacteria, viruses, etc. Antibodies circulate in the blood stream and destroy or inactivate the invaders in a variety of ways.

Arachnid.—A member of the Arachnida, a class of arthropods that includes spiders, ticks, mites, scorpions and some others.

Arbovirus.—One of the group of viruses adapted to life in arthropods and transmitted by them to vertebrate animals. The arthropods concerned are chiefly mosquitoes, sand flies and ticks.

Army ant.—Any of several kinds of ant that travel in large numbers hunting for food. They maintain no permanent nests.

Aroid.—A member of the Araceae or arum family. A familiar example in the United States is the skunk cabbage.

Arthropod.—A member of the phylum Arthropoda, the largest division of the animal kingdom. Arthropods have jointed appendages. Included are crabs, lobsters, millipedes, centipedes, scorpions, spiders, ticks, mites, insects and many minor groups.

Bachac.—The colloquial Trinidadian name for leaf-cutting ants, known also as parasol or fungus-growing ants. They harvest leaves and carry them underground, where a compost is formed to nurture a type of fungus upon which the ants live exclusively.

Bromeliad.—A member of the family Bromeliaceae, or "wild pineapples." Most bromeliads grow on trees, though they are not parasitic. Many have beautiful flowers, and "bromel" fanciers are becoming as familiar as orchid enthusiasts. The "Spanish moss" in our southern states is a bromeliad though not a typical one, for most bromeliads are upright, their leaves flaring like feather dusters.

Cayman.—A group of crocodilians native to Central and South America. Also spelled caiman. In Trinidad, erroneously called alligator.

Cascadoux.—A type of armored catfish, so-called because the body wall is thickly calcified. Eagerly sought by peasants in Trinidad. They say that if a visitor once tastes cascadoux, he will never leave the island.

Chiroptera.—An order of mammals embracing the bats.

Cleistogamous.—Having flowers that fail to open.

Ecdysis.—Molting; shedding the exoskeleton, as in the successive stages of growth of an insect.

Echo-location.—Guidance in flight by means of projecting the voice and noting the time required for an echo to return. Used by some bats not only to avoid striking objects in the dark but also to approach flying prey.

Exoskeleton.—The outer "shell" of crabs, insects, etc., for support of the body. Since the exoskeleton can not grow, it must be shed periodically to permit increase in size of the animal.

Frass.—An entomological term denoting caterpillar droppings.

Hammock.—In the southeastern United States, especially the Everglades, a patch of hardwood forest, usually surrounded by open savannas.

Heliconia.—A plant of the banana family, also called wild plantain. In Trinidad one species, the balisier, has been adopted as the emblem of a leading political party. A favorite of hummingbirds also.

Hesperid caterpillar.—The larva of a skipper butterfly, family Hesperiidae. These caterpillars can be recognized by their slender necks and freely movable heads.

Hymenoptera.—An order of insects including bees, wasps and ants.

Mallophaga.—An order of insects including the so-called biting lice, as opposed to blood-sucking lice. Mallophaga occur chiefly on birds and are often called feather lice in consequence, though a few mallophagans infest mammals. They eat fur and feathers, only rarely taking blood.

Matte.—The colloquial Trinidadian name for a large terrestrial lizard, also called teju, or tegu, *Tupinambis nigropunctatus*. It is an important predator of small wildlife.

Meliponid.—A bee of the family Meliponidae, closely related to honeybees. They are stingless, however. Their hives are located in cavities, which they calk with a waxy cement to prevent entry of marauders.

Myrmecology.—The study of ants.

Orb weaver.—A type of spider that spins a flat web in the form of a wheel, with spokes radiating from a central point and with sticky strands spanning the spokes spirally.

Pathogen.—A living, disease-producing agent, especially microorganisms such as bacteria, viruses, protozoa and fungi.

Pholcid.—A spider of the family Pholcidae, considered rather primitive in the scheme of classification. Pholcids spin untidy webs. The sexes are equal in size. In the United States a familiar pholcid is known as the cellar spider. Pholcids have long legs and small bodies.

Polybiid wasp.—A wasp of the family Polybiidae. Polybiids occur in large colonies in cavities of trees. Many species feed on caterpillars.

Ponerine ant.—An ant of the subfamily Ponerinae, generally of little economic importance. Many feed on floral and other plant secretions, though some live on insect prey.

Primary feather.—A large flight feather on the outer half of a bird's wing.

Rainbird.—The local Trinidadian name for any kind of swift.

Reservoir host.—An animal that harbors agents of disease over long periods of time, thereby enabling the agents to survive adverse periods and to erupt subsequently with the production of renewed outbreaks in other hosts.

Sentinel animal.—An animal—mammal, bird or reptile—deliberately posted in an environment where it may become infected by disease-carrying vectors such as mosquitoes, ticks, etc. Periodic examination of sentinel animals will disclose activity—or inactivity—of such diseases within the areas of exposure.

Serology.—The study of serum—a major component of the fluid fraction of blood. Serum contains antibodies following infection by various microorganisms. Numerous types of serological test are used to identify different classes of antibody.

Skipper butterfly.—A butterfly of the family Hesperiidae. Skippers are classified intermediately between butterflies and moths. They have stout bodies and are strong fliers. Many are inconspicuously marked, and their identification is a matter for the experts.

Solanaceous.—Belonging to the family Solanaceae, the nightshade family, which includes also potatoes, tomatoes and tobacco.

Sonar.—See "echo-location."

Vector.—In medicine, a living transporter of disease agents. Some vectors are only mechanical transporters, e.g., houseflies with their dirty feet. Biological vectors are those in which the disease agents multiply, e.g., malaria organisms in mosquitoes and many viruses in mosquitoes, sand flies and ticks.

Viremia.—A stage early in the course of viral infection during which viruses are circulating freely in the blood stream. It is within this period, usually lasting only a few days, that biting mosquitoes or ticks can themselves become infected. When the viremic host does not die, viremia is followed by immunity and viruses no longer circulate in the blood stream.

Virology.—The study of viruses. In a broad sense this includes not only viruses themselves but also their relationships to infected hosts. In the case of arboviruses, therefore, virology may be considered to include serology, immunology, entomology, mammalogy, ornithology, climatology and a host of related disciplines.

Index